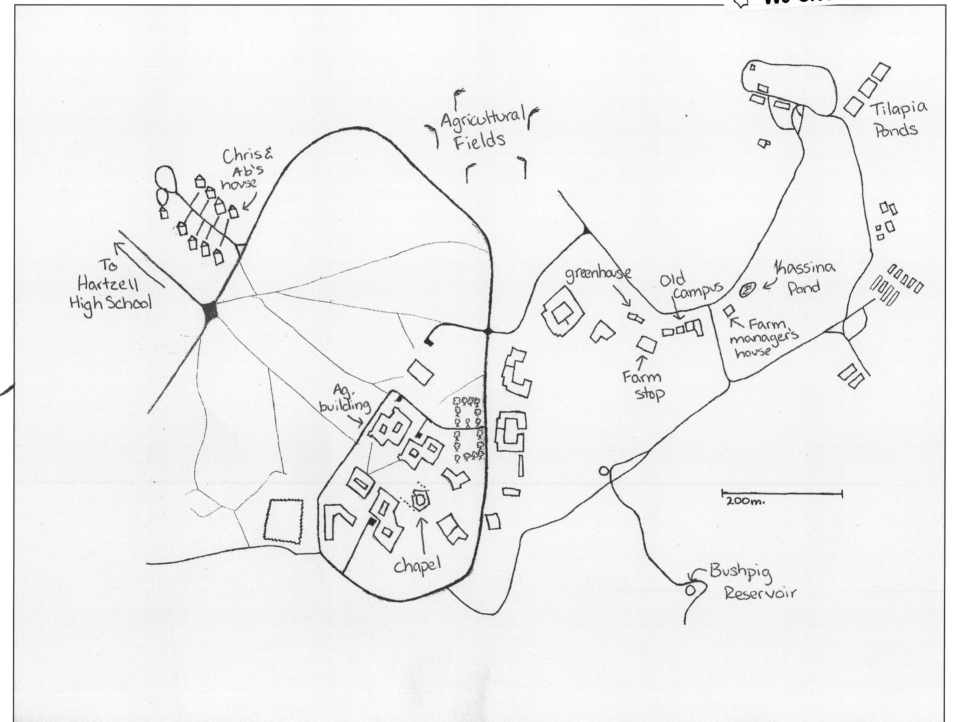

First printing, June 2009

Printed in Korea, Four Colour Print Group

Thy wonders displayed • Africa University
Edited by C.L. "Ab" Abercrombie and Chris Hope

ISBN: 0-9786343-1-4

Text © C.L. "Ab" Abercrombie, G.R. Davis, Terry Ferguson, and Chris Hope
Photography © C.L. "Ab" Abercrombie, G.R. Davis, Terry Ferguson
Jacket photo by Terry Ferguson
Book design by Jo Ann Mitchell Brasington

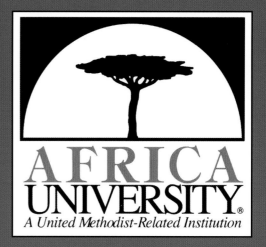

AFRICA UNIVERSITY
A United Methodist-Related Institution

Thy wonders displayed

Africa University

C. L. "Ab" Abercrombie • G. R. Davis • Terry Ferguson • Chris Hope

Foreword by Bishop J. Lawrence McCleskey

I sing th'almighty power of God,
That made the mountains rise,
That spread the flowing seas abroad,
And built the lofty skies.
I sing the wisdom that ordained
The sun to rule the day;
The moon shines full at his command,
And all the stars obey.

I sing the goodness of the Lord,
That filled the earth with food;
He formed the creatures with his Word,
And then pronounced them good.
Lord, how thy wonders are displayed,
Wheree'er I turn my eye,
If I survey the ground I tread,
Or gaze upon the sky!

Isaac Watts, 1674-1746

foreword

by Bishop J. Lawrence McCleskey

Three times in the past 10 years I have been privileged actually to visit Zimbabwe and the campus of Africa University. Reading this book became my fourth visit!

I thought I knew the University, and in a way I did — its main campus, dormitory and classroom and activity buildings, library, administrative offices, and the chapel. This book, however, introduced me to a much larger understanding of the campus — its geological landscape, its wildlife, and its farm. I encountered in a new way the University's creation and inhabitants. The authors' setting of the book in the context of Isaac Watts' hymn is masterful, for this School of Dreams is indeed a manifestation of "th'almighty power of God." The lovingly crafted text is complemented by a striking collection of photographs that bring the campus alive with their witness to the goodness, wonder, and beauty of the place.

Three words from the book describe, for me, its intent and purpose. The authors describe their work as a book about *faith*. It is indeed that, as it is the story of a school founded on faith — faith in God and faith in the power of God to put creation to purposes of goodness and peace. They also describe their book as a narrative about *hope*. It is that as well, for it is the story of how education can explore the natural and human world and enable this world's inhabitants to reach towards their God-given potential. And, the authors say, their book is about *stewardship*. It is that, too, as it tells of a school that is developing a wide range of able and caring leaders for that wonderful part of God's creation known as Africa.

I am grateful to the authors for taking me on this armchair visit to a school they and I love. I am glad you have decided to make this journey as well. One thing I have learned from all my visits to Africa University, the actual ones and this virtual one, is that one cannot experience this remarkable school without wanting to support it. I invite you to join these authors and me in ongoing support of Africa University. You can learn how to do that by visiting the Africa University Development Office website at www.support-africauniversity. org.

Thanks to Ab Abercrombie, G. R. Davis, Terry Ferguson, and Chris Hope for guiding us on this journey and for inspiring us to join them and hosts of others in supporting this venture of faith, hope, and stewardship. In doing so we continue to "sing th'almighty power of God" in a place of astounding dreams and visions.

Bishop J. Lawrence McCleskey
Executive Vice President for Development
Africa University

introduction
Bushpigs, Conservation, and the Gospel

Bushpig
(*Potamochoerus larvatus*)

On the 7th of October, 2007, we — Chris Hope and Ab Abercrombie — were hiking across the A.U. campus, worrying about our classes and our work-permits and all the help we'd need to write this book. Then, suddenly, a bushpig appeared from out of nowhere to stand under the tree *Euphorbia* at the old reservoir on Africa University's near mountain. He was an enormous, rangy boar, maybe pushing 80kg, but for a moment he appeared confused, as if he did not know where he was or what he was supposed to be doing. Then, before the ancient hog vanished into the tall grass, he turned back toward us with a look that was two parts fear and one part hunger.

Bushpigs are not supposed to be seen on exposed, rocky hillsides. And, unlike the males of domestic hogs, a boar *Potamochoerus* usually stays with the sow and her piglets. Of course we could guess some things about this particular boar's biography: we figured that his family had been scattered or was dead, and we knew that his on-campus,

lowland habitat had been subjected to unprecedented human degradation.

We're not going to plead the bushpigs' case. Most folks in Zimbabwe think that the country has plenty of them, and so would you if you'd ever tried to stand between a sounder of *Potamochoerus* and your maize crop. On the other hand, the plight of Old Bushy was related to our vocational difficulties during the last semester of 2007, and it forced us into some unfamiliar moral habitat.

Most people in the U.S.A. — even wildlife professionals — are unaware that the 20th century's most important and innovative game-management strategy (at least for Africa) was developed by a former United Methodist missionary. This is Zimbabwe's *Campfire Program*, a scheme by which "hard currency" derived from high-dollar safari hunting is returned in large part to the local Zimbabweans who share habitat with the trophy animals. The basic principle is sometimes called "value-added conservation." An elephant that's merely a crop-raider is, economically, little different from a 4-ton rat. On the other hand, an elephant whose death by Yankee gunfire will generate a minimum of $20,000U.S. — well, such elephants are creatures to be cherished.

Of course the philosophy underlying "value-added conservation" is not new; U.S. universities have preached it as orthodoxy in their Wildlife Ecology Departments for more than a generation, and user-pay concepts have been fundamental to American game management for nearly a hundred years. So, *Campfire* is not new because it swaps wild animals for dollars. Rather, its innovative brilliance (which derives from the program's Methodist roots) is the idea that most of the hunting-dollars should be returned to the local people as a coherent community, and that the community-as-stakeholder should be involved at a grass-roots level in deciding how the money is to be made and spent.

We shall refrain from discussing *Campfire* further, but we must tell you that it is congruent with our long-held views on conservation. By upbringing and personal conviction, we are members of the

Christian community. As such, we believe that every person has a fundamental vocation of loving and sharing; that is the mandate of the Gospel. It seems to us, however, that the New Testament writers interpreted the teachings of Jesus for a world that was in its Last Days. The early Christians assumed that few tomorrows remained to them, so they should divide all of the world's bounty generously among their sisters and brothers, to meet immediate needs. On the other hand, we are convinced that humanity is <u>not</u> living within the Last Days. (We are teachers, and it's hard to be a teacher unless you believe that your students will see a substantial string of tomorrows.) Therefore, in our opinion, to fulfill the Gospel's mandate of sharing, we must consider not only persons-living; we must also think about the needs of generations yet unborn. In other words, the gospel of conservation is the gospel of sustainability.

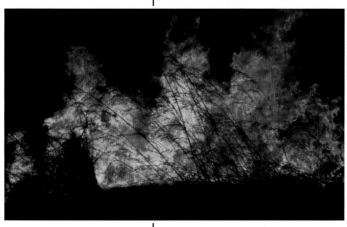

September Grassfire

So, those thoughts are vintage Chris-and-Ab. We know that the concept is pretty simple, but the gospel of sustainability has always seemed true to us, so we've written it and said it and preached it throughout our adult lives. However, our comfortable orthodoxy of sustained-yield conservation was not working on the A.U. campus during the last semester of 2007.

From August through December, we tramped all over that wonderful landscape, spending every spare minute afield. And what did we see? Four human activities dominated the "undeveloped" parts of campus. The grasslands had been burned, in part to facilitate hunting. Subsistence gold panning had increased radically so that the local bottoms of the Mutare River had become a moonscape of exploratory pits. Wildlife snares, targeting critters from twitbirds to bushpigs, had

been set throughout the wildest places. And firewood — oh, Lord, firewood — was being cut and dragged away, ton after ton, every day of the week. We did not have the luxury of gathering quantitative data on these four exploitive practices, but we are certain that they are not sustainable at 2007 levels.

This destruction of campus resources affected us on personal and vocational levels. Even during our first semester at A.U. (1993) we worried about the over-exploitation of University wildlands, and we wanted to do something, but we did not know where to start. Fortunately we soon discovered that we had a powerful ally in our friend, Dr. James Salley. Dr. Salley is a fellow South Carolinian, from Orangeburg, a home-town graduate of S.C. State. He is also A.U.'s most important representative in the United States, working out of the Methodist Vatican in Nashville, Tennessee. And Jim suggested that we could begin by expressing our concern in a book about the Africa University campus.

Therefore, 16 years ago Chris and Ab began talking with Jim about a creating such a book. Originally we envisioned a slick-paged coffee-table volume, illustrating photographically the natural wonders of the University campus. The more we thought about the idea, the better we liked it, and eventually it captured our hearts. In part, this is because we care deeply about the wonderful 600 hectares of Africa where we have been privileged to live. But we've also conceived of the campus, biblically, as a City on a Hill, as a potential model for how undeveloped plots of land could serve as refuge-islands in Africa's increasingly agricultural landscape. We have wanted to do this book a whole, whole lot. We had planned in it to develop the islands-of-habitat model with pictures and words, and we'd hoped to offer this model as a small gift to Africa.

Because we knew the campus well, and because we'd already begun to chronicle the area's biodiversity, we planned to acquire the photographs for our book in a single semester (with help, as you will learn, from Terry Ferguson and G.R. Davis). To this end we drew down our savings accounts, and Jim Salley generously committed the resources of the United Methodist General Board of Higher Education and Ministry. But to tell the truth, that last semester of 2007 was hard going. By luck or persistence we managed to get a few decent pictures of some great critters, and we hope that you will enjoy looking at them. But the campus itself, which had been so bountiful in previous years, was stingy with its animal treasures in 2007: A.U.'s landscapes were being exploited beyond their ability to be generous.

We are not blaming the exploiters. They are not greedy people; they are not trying to get filthy rich. In today's hard times they are just struggling to stay alive and to keep their families going. Metaphorically put, while the ship of Zimbabwe's national economy has foundered, our A.U. campus has become the local lifeboat! And we are thankful for every blessing the lifeboat-campus has given to the desperate communities of Manicaland — for every guinea-fowl supper, for every gram of gold, for every stick of *Acacia* wood that has cooked a child's *sadza*. But the current level of exploitation cannot last, and thus it violates the Chris-and-Ab gospel of sustainability.

We have lain awake through many African nights, thinking upon these things, distressed because in a world of displaced bushpigs and needy people, we do not know exactly what a good steward should do. And that's unfortunate because stewardship is what this book is all about. The problem is — well, we should make a confession — we should admit that we no longer feel qualified to preach our easy gospel of sustainability, for we have not followed the hard, hard Gospel of the New Testament; we have not loved and shared enough.

To complete our confession, let us float the lifeboat analogy a little farther. During the Second World War, the USAT *Dorchester* was struck by torpedoes in the icy waters off the coast of Greenland. Four U.S. Army chaplains — Dutch Reformed, Jewish, Methodist, and Catholic — were aboard the troopship, and they were tasked with

October Hunters
(This photograph was taken by one of our remote trail cameras. The un-cropped original included 1 rifle, 3 men, and 7 dogs.)

loading the lifeboats, which were of insufficient supply. These four gentlemen were faced with heartbreaking questions about who should board the boats *versus* who should not. And indeed the chaplains made some very tough choices — but only after they had joyously given up their own tickets to ride.

In other words, if wisdom comes with sacrifice, we're not there yet, and so, Mr. Bushpig, we too are confused about the new world of new Africa. And like you, we are turning to look over our shoulders. For us, it is from America that we look back toward Africa, from America, the Great, Comfortable Lifeboat in which we sit so safely as we word-process the text of a picture book about your wounded homeland. The sadness in our eyes is two parts fear and one part hunger. But we also want to be like the bushpig in a more positive sense — and like the indomitable tortoises and the magnificent pythons and the ever-present A.U. guineas and the frogs whose songs anticipate the life-giving rains of summer. We want to be like the courageous farm workers, whom you'll meet later on, like Professor Tagwira, who turned down all those high-dollar American jobs, and like Security Guard Zihwa, who has followed the Lord of the Dance through seven decades of African sorrow and joy. We want to hang on in faith, and, by grace, to mix every ingredient of fear and hunger with a dash of fun and a double ration of hope. Thus begins our stewardship plan.

Chris Hope
Ab Abercrombie

Written at Old Mutare, Zimbabwe, 2007, waiting for the rains, and in North Charleston, South Carolina, 2009, waiting to return to Zimbabwe

"And hey, Chrissy! These tiny tracks over here: aren't they bush-piglets?"

Who we are

This book has four authors who love Africa University. We feel compelled to communicate our excitement about the place and our confidence that A.U. will help further the mission of the Church in Africa. All four of us are scientists, hard-core evolutionists who bristle at the very mention of Creationism or Intelligent Design. Furthermore, although we were brought up as traditional Methodists and Catholics, today our concepts of religion are diverse and are sometimes alloyed with doubt. Nevertheless, when push comes to shove — when we consider the gospel of sharing and the irreducible importance of life — we stand within the community of hope. Therefore, if we could sing worth a flip (and one of us actually can), we would, in the pages that follow, "Sing the almighty power of God… [and]…the goodness of the Lord."

Today we all live in South Carolina, and we are all from the South or the Midwest. Collectively, we grew up learning about things like rabbit-dogs, tractors, rocks, lizards, wheat futures, arrowheads, rainfall patterns, and country music. Through a lot of years of schooling, we probably studied too much, and that's one reason we are all college teachers today. Often we'll write in the first person, plural. And when only "*I*" makes sense, we'll tell you who's talking. Now, so that our names might make a little sense to you, we'll introduce ourselves individually.

Ab Abercrombie is a mathematical modeler and a field herpetologist, currently employed by Wofford College in South Carolina. He has taught four semesters in Africa University's Faculty of Agriculture and Natural Resources. G. R. Davis, another Wofford teacher, is an animal physiologist who also specializes in experimental design. G.R. really likes taking pictures, and this is not his first "coffee table" book. Terry Ferguson is Wofford's entire Geology Department. He is also trained as an anthropologist, but his current specialties are geophysics and remote sensing. Chris Hope is a sociologist, though her dissertation research was on non-human primates. She is former chair of the Department of Sociology and Anthropology at the College of Charleston (South Carolina). Chris has taught in A.U.'s Faculty of Agriculture and in the Faculty of Humanities and Social Sciences. We have all tramped many kilometers across the campus of Africa University.

Our mission

In his generous Foreword, Bishop Lawrence McCleskey eloquently explained exactly what we're trying to do. The objective of our book is to guide you on a leisurely tour through A.U.'s larger, unpublicized campus. During this tour you will meet subsistence gold miners, observe elusive wildland creatures, and visit with fascinating people on the A.U. Farm. Sometimes you'll hear too much of our white, American voices during the tour. That's because we'll occasionally call a halt and ask you some difficult questions — questions for which we have no complete answers. But we hope you will forgive us when we seem to lecture (or even to preach); that is certainly not our main intent. Rather, we would show you Africa University: the place and its people and its other creatures. If we are good tour guides, then you will see that our University campus (and we hope you'll come to consider it your University campus) is a microcosm in which a thoughtful observer can celebrate "endless forms most beautiful." So, walk with us across a wonderful landscape.

Structurally, our book consists primarily of three chapters. All four authors worked on every chapter, but we did apportion our efforts a bit according to subject matter and personal interests. In the first chapter we bring you across the ocean to Africa, and then we focus on landscape, hinting at the geological and anthropological complexities of A.U.'s fascinating environs. Woven throughout this material is a discussion about on-campus gold mining, and we use this theme to illustrate the interface between human need, human greed, and the richness of the land. Chris and Ab helped write this chapter, but the ideas and basic organization belong to Terry. Furthermore, this part of your A.U. tour needs to be led by one person, a geoarchaeologist. Therefore, "I" will mean "Terry Ferguson, Professor of Geology and Anthropology." To contrast the brevity of our investigations with the time-depth of our subject, we compressed Terry's work into four composite days, and we wrote the chapter in present tense.

Our second chapter is about campus wildlife. We show you pictures of many creatures and argue that great beauty can be found in small things that are seldom seen. We try to keep in mind the people who make use of the wildlife, and we hint at the ethical complexities of advocating conservation in present-day Zimbabwe. As Chris and Ab wrote this chapter, we came increasingly to see it as a loose-leaf field-guide — with far too many pages blown away by the winds of African change.

In our third chapter we consider the A.U. Farm. This, for us, has been the most difficult chapter to complete because we do not know exactly how to capture an authentic picture of milking stalls and tractor parts and irrigation pipes and wheat fields and resignation and hope. Nevertheless, if you're willing, we'll take you on a tour of the farm. There you will learn about the marvels of milk-cows, the challenges of chickens, and the potentialities of pigs. You will also be introduced to some of the farm's people: you will meet their families, learn about their difficulties, and, perhaps, share some of their dreams. Ab wrote a first-draft introduction and conclusion while Chris collaborated with G.R. on much of the text. The pictures and the basic ideas came from G.R., who also did all the interviews.

Following the last chapter, in a section called "Partnerships," we offer suggestions about how people of faith can contribute to fulfilling the dream and promise of Africa University.

In simplest terms our book describes a small school in a small country. Every modern university publishes a campus "viewbook," and you can consider this to be a viewbook for A.U. At the same time we hope that our book may supply some insights about modern Africa in general, about the inextricably mixed futures of people, agriculture, land, and wildlife in a developing world where life is incredibly beautiful but economic choices are incredibly hard. Essentially, though, this book is a safari into an African landscape that we love. And we have faith that on this safari you'll discover something to cherish.

Good help that we've received

We could not have completed this book without a great deal of assistance. Among those who helped us were:

Jim Salley. Introduced earlier, Jim currently works for the United Methodist General Board of Higher Education in Nashville as A.U.'s Associate Vice Chancellor for Institutional Development. He is our friend and our connection into the power structure of Methodism and the University.

Fanuel Tagwira. When he was Dean of the Faculty of Agriculture and Natural Resources, Dr. Tagwira was Ab's A.U. boss. A fine scientist and generous colleague, "Prof" Tagwira has supported our work on this book in a hundred ways large and small. He is now A.U.'s Vice Chancellor. (That's like an American college president.)

Daniel Nzengy'a. For several years Daniel was the full-time Wildlife lecturer in A.U.'s Faculty of Agriculture. Trained in the best Kenyan tradition of wildlife management, he was an idea-man who would not let us rest, even when we were tired. Good luck, Daniel, in your PhD studies.

The Kies family. Also at A.U., Jane and Larry Kies and their terrifically interesting children helped us learn more about the University farm and about African agriculture in general.

Africa University students. Many of this book's best ideas came from students that Chris and Ab taught at A.U. We remember this long list and name these good people in our thoughts and prayers. From more recent days two young men deserve special recognition. When Ab learned that Terry and G.R. would come help with this book, he recruited two Shona-speaking guides from his biostatistics

Zephania Bonde, recent graduate of A.U.'s Faculty of Agriculture.

Three small notes: First, almost all photographs were made on the University campus; those that were not are clearly indicated. Second, we've included many pictures of many sizes, and we've set aside parts of our chapters by color and font. These layout complexities mean that occasionally the order in which photographs are mentioned in the text will not be exactly the same as the order in which they appear. Third, in formal Zimbabwean English, the use of titles is generally considered the polite form of address, so we shall introduce farm workers as "Mr." or "Mrs." (Chris and Ab inflicted Ms. on our female students at A.U., just as we do in the USA. Because of our status as teachers, this was accepted, albeit grudgingly. On the other hand we believe that to show proper respect, we should address the farm workers according to local custom. We also wish to emphasize the fact that although many farm workers are forced to live apart from their spouses, most of the women are married.)

class. In our "Mountains" chapter you'll meet Mugave Mudiwa, who introduced Terry around Old Mutare and translated his interviews with on-campus gold miners. Zephania Bonde (pictured on the previous page) worked with G.R., enriching his understanding of processes and people at the University farm. All four authors thank you, and we hope that you gentlemen had as much fun as we did.

Other colleagues and institutions

Even before Africa University was granted her charter, United Methodist leaders envisioned Wofford College as her sister institution. Joab Lesesne and Talmage Skinner, respectively Wofford's president and chaplain in the 1990s, encouraged Ab and Chris to work on a book about A.U. Vivian Fisher, retired chair of Wofford's English Department, made helpful comments on several chapter drafts. Dan Maultsby (Wofford '61), Academic Dean-Emeritus of Wofford College, and Dr. Carol Wilson (Wofford '81), Associate Professor of English, proof-read and improved the entire manuscript. With its interest in the African Diaspora, the College of Charleston supported Chris' work in Zimbabwe for two full semesters. Paul Moler, of the Florida Fish and Wildlife Conservation Commission, corrected silly errors in the "Creatures" chapter. Mark Olencki (Wofford '75) advised us about book design; he modestly credits Terry for doing most of the work in the preparation of photographs. Weatherly Meadors (Wofford '09, Biology and Religion) helped with maps and artistic presentation. True to her family's Methodist tradition of selfless service, she refused all compensation. Professor Johnny Lane (Wofford '77), poet and natural scientist, helped in countless ways, the most important of which was re-acquainting us with Jo Ann Brasington (Wofford '89). Jo Ann is the consummate publishing-professional who prepared this book for the printer, performing sundry feats of layout magic and infusing her generous, creative spirit into every page.

8

The view north from Kenya Ridge across the Mutare River toward the A.U. campus
In the left background Old Mutare Mission may be seen at the base of Mt. Chiremba.
To the northeast of this panorama, storm clouds gather.

"...that's a mighty long airplane ride."

Jimmy Buffett

mountains

chapter one

"I sing th'almighty power of God,
That made the mountains rise...."

Isaac Watts

Wofford

College biologist G.R. Davis and I are on our way to Zimbabwe (Fig. 1.1), where we'll help Ab Abercrombie work on a book about Africa University. I am Terry Ferguson, an anthropologist/geologist who studies the processes that create and modify natural and cultural landscapes. My job will be to apply a geo-archaeological perspective toward understanding the past, present, and future of 600 hectares of Zimbabwe called the A.U. campus.

This is my first trip to Africa, and during my trans-Atlantic flight I reflect on how *Homo sapiens* dispersed from that great southern continent around 60 thousand years ago. I wonder why my ancestors in that ancient Diaspora turned north into Europe, and I speculate that I may be the first in my recent line of descent to come home to Africa. I reflect too on how brief my seemingly endless flight actually is. The great-great-grandparents of the slaves who built Wofford's Main Building sailed in chains for seven weeks between the barracoons of Senegal and the markets of Charleston; now, 20 hours out of Atlanta's Hartsfield-Jackson, we are already approaching Zimbabwe. I tell G.R. that in another hundred years, when the oil is gone, intercontinental travelers may be sailing again. G.R. isn't listening; he's focusing his Nikon through the window, trying to get a first picture of Africa. "We're landing now," he says, and as the wheels touch down, I wonder what stories this country and its people might wish to tell us.

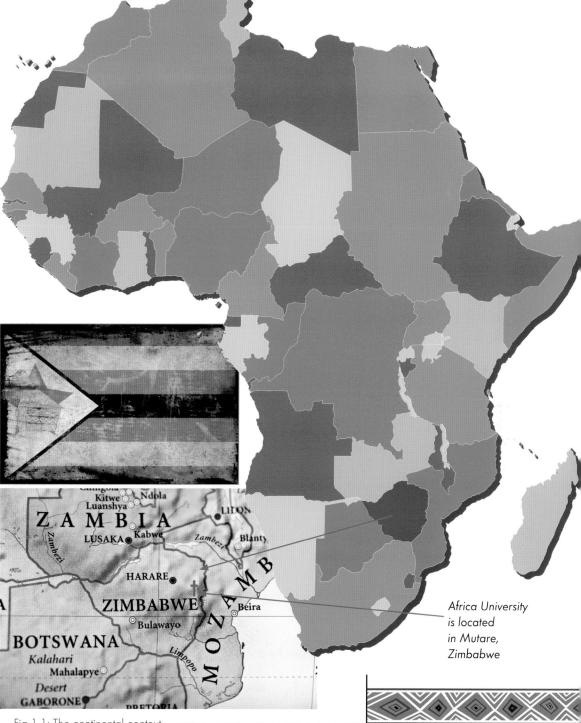

Africa University is located in Mutare, Zimbabwe

Fig. 1.1: The continental context

Fig. 1.2: The Gray Wolf

Fig. 1.3: Traditional housing

Pickup Truck

Our flight arrives at the International Airport in Harare, Zimbabwe's capital. After we clear Immigration and Customs, a university driver, clad in official blue, meets us. He smiles, welcomes us to Africa, loads our baggage into a diesel pickup (Fig. 1.2) that A.U.'s ag students call "the Gray Wolf." Then we depart Harare to the southeast, and we begin to learn first-hand about Zimbabwe.

Seen in the grand perspective of Continent Africa, Zimbabwe is an open woodland, a plateau the size of Montana, bounded on the north and south by rivers, on the west by desert, and on the east by the Afro-Montane Uplift. At the closer scale of a gray pickup truck, however, I perceive Zimbabwe somewhat differently.

The Zimbabwe Plateau is not flat. Between Harare and Rusape we traverse a long series of broad, rolling valleys. On the upgrades I see the determination on the faces of old women, toting firewood on their heads. I hear the whistles of Scotch-cart drivers, encouraging their two-spans of Mashona oxen. On a long downhill run, our driver shuts off his engine and jokes about fuel shortages as we coast, just keeping pace with a grinning boy on a multi-gear bicycle.

The southeastern highway takes us through pastures, fields, and eucalyptus plantations. In the foreground, children in faded uniforms skip along the roadside, laughing about what they did not learn in a hard day of school. Women sell produce — bright piles of tomatoes, or honey, in season — and men carry the hand-tools of agriculture or offer a string of fish taken from a nearby river or reservoir.

A little ways back from the road are thatched huts, sometimes round and traditional, walled with bricks, kiln-baked locally from the red Zimbabwean earth (Figs. 1.3-1.4). The road and strings of houses logically follow the gentler topographic grades, but in the distance — beyond the venders and the huts and the maize fields and the pastures — rugged hills and stark granite outcrops thrust towards the sky (Figs. 1.5-1.6).

After Rusape-town, about two hours out of Harare, our route becomes more southerly, and, through a blue haze in the east, the moun-

Fig. 1.4: Fallow maize field, traditional housing, granite outcrop

Fig. 1.5: Skyline of granite monoliths

Fig. 1.6: Granite bastions of "deep time"

tains of the Mozambican border loom into sight. The surface we now travel is geologically more recent, more complex. The woodlands, though still open, become a bit denser, the trees a little taller, the leaves a little greener. These subtle changes in vegetation are significant for the life of agricultural Zimbabwe. Across the country as a whole, precipitation increases along a west-to-east gradient. Where Zimbabwe meets Botswana, rain is rare; it is concentrated within about eight weeks, and even these weeks may be dry three years out of ten. But as Zimbabwe rises towards the Mozambican border, her seasons become more predictable, her summers wetter.

In eastern Zimbabwe, winter (approximately June through August) is cool and dry, with pleasant, sunny days and crystal-cold nights. Days become windy and warm in September, as the air grows hazy with the smoke from countless grassfires, and by October the weather is almost hot.

November is a month of wishes: the Inter-Tropical Convergence Zone migrates southward, thunderclouds rise in the northeast, and farmers plant their first maize crops, offering with the seed their prayers for generous rain. By mid-December, the strong rains arrive (if they are coming at all), and they will typically continue well into March. Our driver explains these things about the climate in eastern Zimbabwe and also tells us about anomalies in the general pattern, about how one valley may be wet enough to grow bananas while a neighboring valley may be too dry even for maize. When I look out across this complex topography and consider the variable fertility of the soils, I think of a time, not so long ago, when the most productive land was under the control of rich, white farmers, who possessed the money and machinery and big-agriculture know-how to produce enormous harvests that fed much of southern Africa. I catch myself thinking about bushels per acre, like the Brits in "Rhodesia," or cattle per valley, like the Bantu who came here before them. So many people have seen so many dreams, so many possibilities, in this landscape.

For the last few kilometers of the journey, our driver turns left from the Harare-Mutare Highway and heads northward on the Nyanga Road. The land on this last, short stretch is lowland bush, largely unimproved pasture for beef and dairy cattle. This is good land, bottom land, and G.R. comments that people back home might have planted corn/maize in such a place. At a stand of tall trees we cross a concrete bridge over the Mutare River. Another half-kilometer and we can see A.U.'s flags and entrance gate. But before he turns into campus, our driver stops and directs our attention to the left, toward the place where the vision that would become Africa University really began.

Visions

When we look west from the Nyanga Road, we see some small, rectangular houses and, to their right, a double line of gigantic eucalyptus flanking a broad drive that leads to the base of a very high hill. The blue-gum eucalyptus claim Australian ancestry; they are missionary trees, planted long before an American biologist preached his first sermon about the ecological superiority of indigenous vegetation. The avenue of trees leads into Old Mutare, a Methodist mission-station founded by Bishop Joseph Hartzell at the close of the 19th century. The very tall hill above Old Mutare is Mount Chiremba.

Fig. 1.7: Entrance to Old Mutare, looking back toward A.U. (The University's Kwang Lim Chapel is in the background.)

The A.U. Vision: Legends and Historical Notes

Mount Chiremba (Fig. 1.9) is an historic place. According to the local Methodist mythology, when missionary Bishop Joseph Hartzell (Fig. 1.8) arrived in southern Africa, he saw the mountain in a vision. This emboldened Hartzell to approach financier Cecil Rhodes and to cajole that rich imperialist into donating almost 5000 hectares of prime real estate to the American Methodist Church. To celebrate this triumph, Hartzell climbed Mount Chiremba; looking east across the land he had received, he committed it all to God and to the education of Africa. The specifics of this tale remain unverified, but Hartzell was a man to whom heroic legends rightly adhered, and much of the story may be true.

Born on a farm near Moline, Illinois, in 1842, Hartzell received early notice when, in 1863, he risked his life to save four shipwrecked sailors from the icy waters of Lake Michigan. In 1873 he became presiding elder of the New Orleans District of the Methodist Episcopal Church, serving a congregation that had chosen affiliation with the Northern "Free" church after Methodism split over the issue of slavery in 1844. While working in Louisiana, Hartzell faced bitterly entrenched racism with courage and equanimity. He developed an

Fig. 1.9: Mount Chiremba seen from the A.U. campus

abiding interest in the plight of former slaves and, by extension, in the welfare of black Africans generally. Recognizing his dedication and administrative talents, General Conference (the denomination-wide quadrennial meeting) of 1896 designated Hartzell as Missionary Bishop for Africa. Methodism's founder, John Wesley, had claimed the world as his parish. Bishop Hartzell had not been assigned quite so much territory, but still, he had Africa, a big continent, and he wanted to cover it all. So, in the days before airplanes and Land Rovers, the Missionary Bishop and his wife moved a lot. Indeed, one account notes that they traveled over 1.3 million miles to promote Methodist education in Africa, using every available means of transportation from ocean steamer to oxen back. One of these journeys brought him to Mount Chiremba, to his meeting with Cecil John Rhodes, and to the vision that Hartzell would maintain throughout his life.

Years before Hartzell came to Africa, Zimbabwean Chief Tendai, of the Manyika Land Shona, had his own vision about the direction African history might take. Hoping to prepare his people for the future, the chief swapped a vast tract of land to the British South Africa Company (the BSAC, Rhodes' outfit), in exchange for "educational opportunities and guns." On Tendai's old land, near the foot of Mount Chiremba, the BSAC briefly maintained a regional headquarters they called Umtali (a name from which the present-day "Mutare" is derived). By the mid-1890s, however, BSAC engineers had admitted that they could not push a practicable railroad over steep and high Christmas Pass, about a dozen kilometers south of Mount Chiremba. This meant that the company, whose visions of commerce were global, could not maintain easy traffic between Umtali and the Indian Ocean, so the BSAC decamped to the port of Beira, in Portuguese East Africa (now Mozambique). Thus, the land was available for other uses.

A.U. historians speculate on whether Hartzell was very persuasive and Rhodes very generous — or whether the company merely wanted to dump its devalued land and its educational commitments onto the shoulders of American do-gooder missionaries. But in any case, the Methodist Church received the old BSAC holdings. So Tendai's land became Rhodes' land, which became Hartzell's land.

Today the land is bisected by the Nyanga Road. Africa University is on the east side. On the west is the United Methodist mission-station of Old Mutare (Fig. 1.7).

This enterprise, standing in the shade of Mount Chiremba, includes staff residences, an orphanage, a hospital, and a church. To address the educational mission of Old Mutare, there is Hartzell School.

Although one cannot know the precise sort of "educational opportunities" Chief Tendai hoped to secure by means of his land-swap, there is no doubt that, over the years, Hartzell School has been a success. This became strikingly clear during and immediately after Zimbabwe's war for independence. Hartzell graduates were leaders in the long struggle against white-minority rule. After victory had been achieved, they became powerful advocates for reconciliation with the nation's former oppressors. Today alumni from Old Mutare are still recognized as leaders — particularly in agriculture, ministry, and medicine — throughout southern Africa and the world.

Fig. 1.10: The chapel at Hartzell School

Fig. 1.11: Looking west-northwest from A.U. Campus, the University's Kwang Lim Chapel is in the foreground. Across the distant Nyanga Road is the eucalyptus avenue leading to Old Mutare Center (background).

18

Seeing the University

Ab had earlier emailed that a student would give me a tour of Old Mutare, so I indicate that our driver can skip Hartzell Mission for now and turn directly into Africa University. We clear front-gate security with no hassles and drive up the straight road pointing from Old Mutare to A.U.'s Kwang Lim Chapel (Fig. 1.11). We are, at last, on campus.

From University web pages and Ab's email, G. R. and I have some advance information about A.U. At the close of the 19th century, Bishop Hartzell had dared to dream about Methodist higher education in Africa. This dream moved toward reality in 1984 when a committee of African bishops petitioned General Conference that a university should be established, soon, perhaps on the land across the Nyanga Road from Mount Chiremba and Old Mutare Mission. An enabling resolution was unanimously ratified four years later, and in January of 1992, Robert Mugabe, Zimbabwe's president, signed an official charter, making Africa University the first private university in Zimbabwe and the first United Methodist institution of higher education on the continent.

Classes began that same year with a handful of students divided between the Faculties of Agriculture and Theology. ("Faculties" at A.U. are like Colleges or Schools within American universities.) On 17 December, 1994, the first graduates received their degrees. The University added a Faculty of Management and Administration in 1995, a Faculty of Education in 1996, a Faculty of Humanities and Social Sciences in 1998, and a Faculty of Health Sciences in 2004. Today the University enrolls about 1000 students, split among six Faculties and the A.U. Institute for Peace, Leadership, and Governance. These young women and men come from almost 30 nations and represent perhaps a hundred socio-cultural traditions. Like university students everywhere, they attend class and study and play sports and worship and raise hell and occasionally tote laundry home to momma. They also pursue dreams that would make Chief Tendai and Bishop Hartzell (and perhaps even Cecil Rhodes) very proud.

A.U.'s students and classes and teachers — indeed, the University's entire academic sector — have been extensively celebrated in pamphlets, books, brochures, filmstrips, videos, websites, lectures, and sermons. But there are also other worlds on Chief Tendai's land. These are worlds that few visitors see; they are also the worlds we have come to document in words and pictures.

Day 1: Seekers

Our driver lets us out in front of Ab's house on Faculty Row. G.R. and I stay only long enough to drop our bags and change into field clothes. Though tired from our short/forever journey, we're off for a walking recon of the south campus, across the Mutare River (Fig. 1.12). Ab wants to take advantage of sunny weather and the remaining hours of daylight.

During a good year, December brings the first strong rains to Old Mutare. Thus far, 2007 is looking good: the rainy season has already settled the dust, puddled the roads, and slicked up the exposed mud. G.R., Ab, and I hike south, skirting the A.U. soccer fields and traversing a muddy kilometer of scrub that burned in a September fire. Ab explains about the fire, talks about the rains, requests that we photograph a pair of mating grasshoppers (Fig. 1.13). "The green clump of trees ahead," he says, "that tangle yonder with the palms — that's where we can cross the river."

As we climb down the steep northern bank of the Mutare, G.R. descends a bit more rapidly than he'd intended, mud-skiing on the seat of his pants, with a camera tripod as his ski pole. More careful

Fig. 1.12: Ab and G.R. traverse Kenya Ridge as sunny Day 1 breaks into rain.

now, we take our time crossing the river, balancing on a log half a meter above the churning, muddy water.

After we climb up the bank on the Mutare's south side, we encounter numerous deep, vertical shafts that have been dug by subsistence gold miners into the alluvial sediments along the river (Fig. 1.14). The shafts are generally about one by two meters across and extend two to ten meters straight down into the alluvium. Some are recent, their edges sharp, their bottoms scarcely discernible in the cool blackness below. Other shafts have collapsed, and I wonder whether the slumped earth might cover the remains of some miner, caught below the surface when a split-second cave-in occurred.

Beyond the honeycomb of poor-folks' hand-dug shafts, we come upon the foundations of the Bulldog Mine, a commercial operation of decades past. Concrete slabs and skeletons of rusting metal mark places where buildings and mining equipment once stood. From Bulldog's ruins, we begin our ascent of Kenya Hill, toward the ridge that marks the southern border of the University campus. We follow old roadbeds that had begun as footpaths and are becoming footpaths again. Ab says, "I think this 'un used to go all the way to Mozambique, back in the day."

At a turn on the Kenya Hill road, we meet a group of subsistence gold miners. Six young men — Ab and Chris had been seeing that number here for months — are digging with hands and hard-worn

Fig. 1.13: Grasshoppers along trail

Fig. 1.14: Looking down mine shaft into the alluvial deposits along the Mutare River

Fig. 1.15: Snail

tools around dolerite boulders shaped like gigantic cannon balls (Fig. 1.16). Their work area extends a few meters along the roadbed and up the steep slope of the mountain. We exchange greetings with the miners; we smile, we wave, and then we continue climbing the Kenya Hill ridge. These miners are one of my main reasons for coming to Africa, but I know that I will see them again in a day or two, and I'll bring a native Shona speaker with me. Today I do not wish to start on the wrong foot with these miners, and I'm unsure of how my American colloquial English might sound to Zimbabwean ears.

As we depart, I turn back to wave at the miners. One young man is already digging again. He pries with an iron bar, his head and chest beneath a boulder half the size of a Chevy pickup. Apparently this miner's need for gold overrides any concern about the law of gravity. I think of the collapsed shafts down along the river and again feel uneasy. As we continue up the ridge, the valley's excellent acoustics bring us the sounds of other miners, digging and sluicing in the river sands and red water.

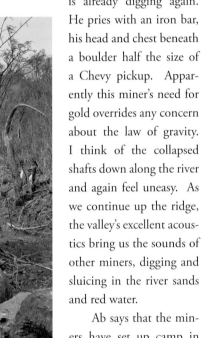

Ab says that the miners have set up camp in an abandoned shaft near the top of Kenya Hill. Respecting their privacy, we decide against proceeding to the summit. Ab reminds us that he needs to pick up two remote "critter cameras" that he'd set on a bat colony. He points on up the road. "When we get to that switchback, we can cut cross-country."

On the switchback promontory, I look back, across the place of our boulder-miners, across the river, across the A.U. academic campus and northwest to Old Mutare Mission. The campus vista and the ridges beyond present a spectacular panorama (page 9). And, of more immediate relevance, the approach of a swirling, black, storm front adds a quantum of genuine awe. Still, I remind myself, this is agricultural Zimbabwe in December: rain is definitely supposed to be good.

As the first drops begin to fall, we eat a quick lunch — peanut butter sandwiches and small bananas, badly squashed in G.R.'s daypack. Ab looks at the exposure counters on his trail cameras; he cusses trail cameras in general and these two trail cameras in particular. I note the building storm and ask if there is any way we can avoid the slippery banks and crossing logs of the Mutare River. Ab says we can hike back to the Nyanga Road and return to campus by the front gate. G.R. fumbles through a wealth of Ziploc bags, armoring his beloved cameras against the deluge. "Oh, all right," he says, "let's go." I glance toward a jumble of stones on my right. A snail on the rocks seems unperturbed by the change in the weather (Fig. 1.15).

As we walk the shoulder of Kenya Ridge, the rain intensifies. Before we hit the Nyanga Road, we are in a downpour that would have accelerated Noah's ark construction. By the time we reach the campus gates, I can testify first-hand to the generosity of December rains in southern Africa. The University's security guards stare dubiously at the three soggy white men — who look more than a little like drowned lab rats — presenting themselves at the entrance to campus. "I ain't getting out my ID in this rain," Ab grins, and then the guards laugh and let us pass. In spite of my poncho and the boots I'd too hastily "water-proofed," I conclude my first adventure to the south end of campus drenched to the bone. But I am exhilarated by the prospect of learning more about this beautiful and intriguing landscape, about its people, and about the ongoing quest for gold in the hills of eastern Zimbabwe.

Fig. 1.16: Gold miners back in October 2007

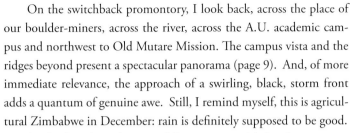

Fig. 1.17: Rusting parts of a ball mill at Magician Mine

Fig. 1.18: Unfinished soapstone sculpture

Fig. 1.19: Pieces of stoneware plate

JINING CLASSICS
STONEWARE
4129
MADE IN CHINA

Day 2: Fragments of Earth

I awake just past dawn on my first full day in Africa. I lace up my semi-dry boots, slip a new card into my digital camera, and check the equipment in my field pack. After a breakfast of Zimbabwe Pro-Nutro Cereal and a painful hit of G.R.'s anti-jetlag coffee, we set off toward the Mutare Valley. Our plan for the morning is to stay on the river's north side and check out an abandoned mining site.

Serenaded by the "Wake up..." calls of dark-capped bulbuls, we cut across A.U.'s academic campus and intersect an old roadbed that's now little more than a trail. We skirt the west end of the ridge with the cross; we wave to workers from the University pump station and turn east along a terrace above the Mutare River. About half a kilometer beyond the pump-station turnoff we reach our morning objective, Magician Mine. This mine, like Bulldog, had been a big commercial operation in pre-University times. We observe deep cuts into the bedrock, their tailings now fringed by the recovered acacia woodland.

G.R. sets up his tripod to photograph a platoon of termite soldiers; Ab rescues a toad trapped in a large concrete cistern. I slip into archaeologist mode.

The territory around Magician Mine is scarred by eroded shafts and rusting metal (Fig. 1.17). Here a crusher-machine pulverized ore-rock into dust; there a rectangle of small stones marked the border of a flower garden. I pace distances and note directions. I pause to photograph unfinished pieces of contemporary soapstone sculpture (Fig 1.18), abandoned after their carvers discovered structural cracks across the arms of Methodist crosses or in the grain of other tourist-ware figures. Then, amid this detritus of metal and soapstone, I spy ceramic artifacts. These fragments, made of earth, tell us very little concerning the enterprise of hard-rock mining at Magician; instead, they speak about the people who worked at this site. Ab holds up two

Fig. 1.20: Earthenware vessel fragment

Fig. 1.21: Cutting grass

Fig. 1.22: Mr. Joseph Kabera reading his notebook and tending goats

pieces of a stoneware plate (Fig. 1.19), brought here by Europeans, who mined Magician from the time of Rhodes until mid-20th century. The clay for this plate was dug, glazed, and fired in China, of course, like so much of the middle class dinnerware "back home" in Victoria's England. The antecedents of other pottery are more local. I find fragments of a small earthenware vessel (Fig. 1.20), four pot shards, which fit together as certainly as the coasts of Africa and South America. The contour of the pot directly reflects the pressures of the potter's hand. The exterior surfaces of the four shards are thickly blackened with soot, indicating repeated use above small cook-fires. Viewed together, the Chinese stoneware and the earthen pot paint a picture of the past. In my mind's eye, I see an afternoon in the early 20th century. Magician's European supervisors sit at a table in the mine's office, eating tea sandwiches from an imported china plate. In the sun outside, native miners tend their fire, warming *sadza* or vegetables in the pot that they will share....

My mental picture is shattered by a familiar voice: "So how old is that priceless artifact?" Ab knows that archaeologists hate the age-question, and he probably asks it with malice and aforethought. Because of the pot's condition and design, I'm reasonably confident that it's from the 20th century. "Five thousand years," I reply, "at least." Ab laughs and reports that he knows of another broken pot, along a ridge behind the A.U. chicken houses. "I think I can find it after lunch," he says, "but I'm a long way from sure." I ask why he didn't take a GPS reading. "It's just another old pot," he shrugs, "I was looking for hingeback tortoises." Old pots definitely do not speak to Ab; perhaps tortoises do.

In spite of a diligent search, we find no more fragments of either the china plate or the earthen vessel. Meanwhile, the rusting pieces of machinery pose more questions than they answer. I have no clear picture of how this equipment was used. I will have to wait until I can revisit the Magician site with someone who knows about commercial mining technology.

After a lunch of *sadza* and collards in the A.U. dining hall, we head out along the asphalt road that leads northeastward through the University Farm. Playing tour guide, Ab indicates the old farm buildings, where all of A.U.'s classes were conducted during the early 1990s. "Statistics..." — he points with a snake-stick — "...theology, rural sociology, computer science...." Through an open window I see a steaming cook-pot; diapers dry on a porch clothesline. Men cut grass with long machetes (Fig. 1.21), and small children sail leaf-boats in flooded potholes. G.R. sets up his tripod; we leave him here to begin his study of the agricultural campus and its people.

At the farm manager's house, Ab and I turn right onto a dirt road that cuts through a small herd of goats, browsing on newly-greened vegetation. We stop and talk to a man who sits atop a stack of bricks, watching the goats (Fig. 1.22). A woman passes, carrying a large jug of milk on her head. I call to her and ask if I can take her picture. She agrees, though I can tell she is not very happy about it. She smiles broadly when I suggest a second photograph, without the jug on her head (Fig. 1.23). I think I understand.

We wave goodbye and begin our ascent of the ridge, following a narrow gravel road. We wind past the circular reservoir that feeds A.U.'s irrigation system; Ab says something about white-toothed shrews and points uphill. I nod, and we walk on. At the crest of the ridge we go left, along a spine of dark rocks; a turn to the right would have taken us to the base of the cross that dominates the campus skyline.

"I'm sure it's up here somewhere," Ab says. He's supposed to be seeking the vanished pot, but when I don't watch him carefully, he starts turning rocks, looking for geckos. Still, knowing Ab as I do, I am not entirely surprised when we eventually locate the pot shards, back under a low overhang of rock (Figs. 1.24-1.25). I unpack my GPS, ruler, camera, and field book to record the find in context. Though similar in shape to the earthenware vessel we'd seen at Magician, this pot is much bigger, and it is of a type used historically in southern Africa to carry and store water. We find, in all, 10 shards.

As I begin sketching the lay of the shards, Ab again goads me to speculate about age. "This looks older than the pot we found this morning," I say, "but, without radiocarbon dating, who knows whether it's from 1960 or 1690." Silently I wonder if the vessel might be even older; its unornamented design is an enduring standard. I say that I can imagine somebody carrying the pot up the steep slope to our south — like the woman we'd seen with the milk jug. "It would have been a skinny girl," Ab nods, "maybe 13, balancing 10kg of water on her short Shona haircut." Then he admits he could be wrong. "Look at it this way," I suggest. "We found the pot hidden under a rock overhang, near a principal trail leading from Mozambique down into the Zimbabwe lowlands. Maybe somebody was using it to cache food or other supplies."

I pick up one of the shards, hold it in my hand, and think about a time when the molding and firing of clay stood at the pinnacle of technology. I number this first shard, wrap it, and talk to Ab about the brief centuries between ancient humanity's pre-pottery millennia (baskets, stone bowls, skin bags…) and our own eye-blink decades of petroleum-based plastics. "Pottery came to Zimbabwe from Africa's north," I say, "like so many other things."

* * *

Fig. 1.23: Milk from the farm's store (You'll meet Mrs. Mary Makute and other farm workers in Chapter 3.)

When I stand and stretch and actually look to the north, I think about my old mentor and colleague, the late petroleum geologist John Harrington. "What do you see?" he would ask in a place like this. And if I should answer, "Trees and fields and ridges beyond ridges," I'd have little hope of passing his course. "Wrong, lad," Harrington would admonish; "you see a thousand ancient Bantu warriors, driving their cattle across the green Zambezi River." Ab, by contrast, would insist that the Zambezi was way too far to see, and that, in any case, Zimbabwe's Department of Veterinary Services would never allow Zambian cattle across the country's northern border. If I should decide to argue the point, Ab might concede that Harrington could be right. Of the clearings that we can see in the misty north, many are being browsed by goats or grazed by cows. And African historians know that Zimbabwe became pastoralists' country only after the Bantu cattle had eluded the Zambezi River's abundant crocodiles.

Whatever Ab's obstinacy about "seeing" cattle in the Zambezi, he does not argue against the historical importance of the Bantu migrations. The word itself, *Bantu*, is a term employed by non-specialist

Fig. 1.24: Rockshelter containing pottery

Fig. 1.25: Pottery shards under rockshelter, a few leaves cleared away

23

anthropologists (like me) to designate several groups of farmer/pastoralists who spoke related languages and came to southern Africa from what we now call eastern Congo and Tanzania. Nobody knows exactly when the Bantu entered Zimbabwe. But before they arrived, indigenous people had gathered plants and killed animals in that land for many millennia. These early inhabitants spoke what we term Khoisan languages, so they are sometimes collectively called "Khoisa." Like all other representatives of our species, the Khoisa were extremely intelligent. They knew the places of plants, the habits of animals, the times of weather and climate. They sat or squatted around fires at night, telling great or small stories — about the nature of God, or about the wisdom of bees and the foolishness of boys who raided beehives with insufficient smoke. They feared death, loved children, and knew the contours of their landscape with the precision of a GPS receiver. Archaeologists have learned little else about the history of these people in eastern Zimbabwe; few of their tools survived the humidity of two thousand rainy seasons, and, in any case, their population densities were so low that encountering their relics is a matter of great good luck. Still, when the Bantu came, they entered a land where people had lived for a very long time — yet where the human environmental impact had been near zero.

The Bantu, on the other hand, brought cattle. Ecologically, this was not entirely bad news, for the grasses and forbs of the Zimbabwe Plateau had co-evolved with hard-grazing mammals for 35 million years. Still, there was the matter of density. For the pastoralists from the north, the possession of cows signified social status, and a man could not have too many of them. Furthermore, the tsetse fly was absent from Zimbabwe, and therefore trypanosomiasis did not initially limit cattle density. Because cows (and, to a lesser extent, goats) provided an easy, reliable source of food, human densities of the early pastoralists could vastly exceed those of the earlier hunter-gatherers.

The invaders from the north would change Zimbabwe forever, not just because of their cattle but because of the entire suite of cultural adaptations they ferried across the Zambezi River. For instance, the Bantu brought techniques of construction with stones, and from the exfoliating granite of Zimbabwe's mountains they built corrals to protect their precious cattle from the lions of darkness. Of course, human dwellings could also be made of stone. Defensive outposts and religious structures on the tops of many mountains and hills give further evidence of Bantu masonry skills. And Bantu-built Great Zimbabwe, a few hours south of Old Mutare, is a world-famous, castle-like edifice, approximately 100m by 70m in extent, with walls 10 meters high and seven meters thick.

In addition to cattle and masonry, the northerners also imported their iron-smelting techniques, which had been refined in Africa while northern Europe still lagged in the Stone and Bronze Ages. The ridges of eastern Zimbabwe were rich in ore, and vast mopane woodlands provided trees for charcoal, so iron metallurgy flourished in the Bantus' new country. Some scholars claim that weaponry was the central innovation. Indeed, iron spear points were the epitome of military hardware, and before too many centuries the Bantus would fight their wars — first against one another, and later against European invaders from the south.

Meanwhile, even as Zimbabwean ironsmiths were producing spear points, they also forged durable axe- and hoe-blades. In my opinion, these were vastly more important than weapons because the northern pastoralists brought cleared-land agriculture south with them.

Initially Bantu agriculture revolved chiefly around millets. "Millet" is not a single species of plant, nor does the term designate a botanically meaningful set of species. Instead, millets comprise an agricultural category of small-seed, low-moisture, rapidly maturing grains that have been grown for over four millennia in Africa and South Asia. Most photosynthesize through a 4-carbon pathway and can therefore make efficient use of CO_2 in the arid tropics. Because millets are drought-resistant, and because the seeds store exceedingly well, these grains have been important in African peoples' risk-avoidance strategies. Also, many millets contain a substantial amount of the amino acid methionine, which is critically lacking in the maize products which would eventually replace most millet culture.

Today the millets most commonly grown in Zimbabwe are probably pearl millet, *Pennisetum glaucum*, and finger-millet, *Eleusine coracana*. Although the latter is also widely grown in India, both species are of African origin. (*Panicum miliaceum*, the millet well known to Americans as birdseed, was probably domesticated in northern China.)

For the Bantu cowherds seeking to supplement a diet of milk and beef, millets had substantial advantages. Because these indigenous grains are drought-adapted, during bad years a field of millet doesn't produce a whole lot less than it does during good years. These roughly constant yields of early Zimbabwe's grain staple damped the effects of an unpredictable climate on human society. In pre-colonial Zimbabwe, human populations might not have been particularly dense, but actual famine was comparatively rare.

The relative stability of millet agriculture was shattered by the arrival of another grain into old Zimbabwe. Corn (*Zea mays*; in Zimbabwean English you may expect to hear it called corn, maize, or mealies) is a product of the Americas. First cultured in Mexico at least 7000 years ago, the grain underwent rapid agricultural selection and spread across much of the New World. Corn was immediately accepted as good food by the European invaders of America's shores, and about eight years after it was "discovered" by Columbus, *Zea mays* was introduced into Africa. In theory, corn may have drifted into Zimbabwe from the north, like millets, cows, and the working of iron. But I consider that route unlikely, and in any case I am confident that the extensive Zimbabwean culture of *Zea mays* was a product of European intervention from the south. Today corn is the agricultural staple of Zimbabwe. *Sadza*, which is like thick, stiff grits, is made from corn and is eaten with almost every meal (Fig 1.26).

Corn is unlike millets in several respects. While millets are troublesome to prepare and have wretched bread-making qualities, corn is easily prepared for the table. The caloric yield of a millet crop is predictably modest, but corn can produce enormous amounts of food per unit-area of land. However, the mega-productivity of corn is highly dependent on the availability of water. Thus, in a climate like eastern Zimbabwe's, the culture of corn, unlike that of millet, tends to be a boom-or-bust kind of thing. Because corn can be so productive, it is a grain well suited

Fig. 1.26: What to order in A.U.'s cafeteria: "Sadza, beans, and vegetables, please ma'am."

More on the Khoisa, the Cows, and the Bantu

The date of the Bantu "invasion" into southern Africa, probably occurring in poorly-defined waves, is subject to debate. Some researchers suggest that it began as early as 1500 to 1000 BC. Pottery fragments and cow bones along the upper Zambezi have radiocarbon dates around 380 BC. For Zimbabwe as a whole, current archaeological evidence indicates the presence of iron, pottery, and cereal agriculture by 0 BC / AD.

We are reasonably confident about our assertion that disease did not severely limit Zimbabwe's cattle-density in early Bantu times. Nowadays, however, bovine trypanosomiasis is prevalent in 10% of the country; raising cattle in these tsetse areas is difficult, particularly for poor people. During Zimbabwe's recent economic/political troubles, cattle farmers have reported outbreaks of other diseases (including anthrax and hoof-and-mouth), which formerly had been well controlled.

The fate of Zimbabwe's Khoisan-speaking hunter-gatherers after the Bantu expansion is not completely known. Overall, it appears that most of the early inhabitants were somehow pushed off their land by the newly arrived farmer/herders. Some were probably killed; others may have intermarried. A few bands could have moved westward, hoping to maintain their old way of life in the deserts of what would become Botswana. On the other hand, there are indications that some Khoisan groups adopted pastoralism coincident with or even prior to the arrival of the Bantu-speaking agriculturalists; these folks might have been assimilated into the developing societies of ancient Zimbabwe. Several of these hypotheses could be investigated using modern genetic techniques.

for societies that intend to export much of their agricultural produce, and it frees a substantial portion of the population from the necessity of agricultural labor. The society imposed by Great Britain upon Zimbabwe depended upon a surplus of labor beyond subsistence needs. The British exploited this labor in a number of ways — for public works, for the production of cash crops, for village-level administration, for the conduct of war — but, as we shall see, the most important of these Eurocentric enterprises was mining.

* * *

My field notes are now complete. I draw a double line across the page; I slip the notebook into my pack, next to the Ziploc bag of pot shards. I take a final set of context photos and then set off with Ab, back down the trail toward A.U.'s academic campus. Along the way we stop to examine an outcropping of highly sheared rock. The outcropping exhibits an alignment of minerals that geologists call foliation. This is a property of certain rocks that have been altered by heat and by regional metamorphic compression applied perpendicularly to the visible planes, usually several kilometers deep in the earth. With the electronic compass of my GPS receiver, I determine that the alignment of the foliation is almost exactly east-west (Fig. 1.27). Since my arrival at Africa University I have observed this same compass orientation

in several different outcrops, at several different places. This pattern indicates that in the distant past, stupendous pressures were applied from north and south. Such enormous compressional forces are associated only with tectonic events. These events involve the jostling of continent-sized fragments of the earth's crust, which are moved as if on a conveyor belt by convection currents deep in the earth.

After a long moment I turn and look west, across a panoramic vista that encompasses a hemisphere of African sky and the northern half of A.U.'s campus. (See picture on page 10.) Drifting into a geologist's reverie, I think back across 2.9 billion years to a time when the jostling fragments of earth began to collide and form an ancient continent. I see kilometers deep within the earth, where rocks flow like taffy, hot enough to melt, yet, by pressure, unmelting; I see those rocks cooling slowly, over a thousand ages. Even deeper in the earth, where temperatures are hotter than Dante dared imagine, molten rock — the magma — rises toward earth's surface. Some of this liquid rock breaches the crust to form the ocean floor. Some blasts skyward and rains as volcanic lava and ash on land and sea. Some cools in pockets, kilometers deep within the earth.

By about 2.6 billion years ago, these tectonic forces have formed the rocks that will become Zimbabwe. But the rocks, once formed, do not rest unchanged. Even as the proto-continent is born, I watch the forces of erosion begin to wear it down. Dust-sized fragments of earth wash to the ocean, and on the sea floor they mingle with a continuing accumulation of volcanic debris. I see these deep sediments changed by time and pressure, their layers folded upward from the depths by movements of earth's continually shifting fragments. I see repeated cycles of such exultation and making-low, an unceasing struggle between tectonic uplift and the patient power of flowing water to wear away kilometers of rock, again and again. The landscape we call A.U.'s campus reflects the most recent episodes of Africa's uplift and erosion. This all seems quite clear to me, so, because I'm feeling poetical, I tell Ab that we walk today upon the latest footprints of the continuing "Dance of the Continents." (Readers with more interest in the tectonic events that formed Zimbabwe are referred to this chapter's Appendix 1, "More Geology.")

Unless you're talking about reptile biogeography, it's hard to interest Ab in dancing continents, but he does care about the structure of A.U.'s campus, and the ancient events of deep Earth are directly relevant to that subject. Africa University is located on the western edge of a region of Zimbabwe known as the Eastern Highlands. And ever since the most recent uplift of this region, the area around campus has been continuously eroded by the Mutare River and its tributary, the Nyagambu.

The Mutare River flows through the southern portion of the campus, from east to west. It has cut a deep, narrow valley into metavolcanic and metasedimentary rocks that comprise what geologists call a greenstone belt (Appendix 1). In the present age, several meters of alluvial sediments cover the bottom of A.U.'s Mutare Valley. These sediments are the product of weathering, erosion, transportation, and deposition of the greenstone-belt rocks that make up the adjacent slopes and ridges. The presence of on-campus gold (to be discussed under the "Day 3" heading) is directly related to the greenstone belts and to the sediments whittled from them.

Meanwhile, on the central and northern portions of campus, by cycles of erosion and flood, of carving and deposition, the Nyagambu River and its small tributaries have flattened the land across a much wider area. Today, most A.U. farming takes place within this ancient floodplain, and the richness of the soils reflects in large part the mineral content of these sediments.

These same soils grew wild plants for the Khoisa, millet and maize for the Bantu, wheat for the Euro-farmers of mid-century. Now they provide meals for the University cafeteria, employment for the A.U. farm workers, study-plots for ag students and their professors. Developing strategies for the sustainable use of African soils is a high-priority mission for the University's Ag School and for the A.U. Farm, where G.R. has spent the afternoon learning about farming practices in modern Zimbabwe.

By the end of the day, we're all tired. I organize my field notes while Ab cooks a supper of beans and fake rice that's made from broken corn. G.R. slices tomatoes and tries to make Ab feel guilty about having a stove that would be the envy of any farm-worker family. Af-

Fig. 1.27: Sheared and foliated rock showing east-west structural trend

ter we eat, we discuss such things as the wisdom of sustainable agriculture while we crowd around my computer, enjoying the rare luxury of electricity and downloading our digital pictures. The computer screen may lack the old-Africa charm of an acacia campfire, but here we are, perhaps not unlike the Khoisa, sitting close to the small light, recounting, reflecting.

Day 3: Of Gold and Miners

On the morning of my third day at Africa University, I am introduced to my Shona-speaking assistant, Mugave Mudiwa, who'd been a star in Ab's biostatistics class the previous semester. Mugave — yes, he's been teased sufficiently about the similarity of his name and President Mugabe's — is from Old Mutare. His knowledge of the people

Note on Professional Ethics

In this section and again in the "Day 4" section, I write about some mining activities that are not legally sanctioned. The professional ethics of my academic disciplines require that I protect the anonymity of my informants. Also, the miners who agreed to be interviewed and photographed did so with the understanding that I would not reveal their identities. Therefore I do not report these people's names. Enlargement of my photographs for purpose of identification would be considered a violation of international copyright laws.

I applied the same ethics when I interviewed people at the Hartzell Mission about sensitive political topics, substituting the last name of a well-known Zimbabwean political family as a pseudonym for their actual surname.

and the region will prove invaluable over the coming days. As we sit in Ab's office, I learn a little bit about him, his life at A.U., and growing up in Zimbabwe.

"I was born just across the Nyanga Road and went to school at the Old Mutare Mission," Mugave speaks softly. "I am now a second-year agricultural student." The young man smiles. He looks down at his hands with a politeness I have noticed in several African students. I ask Mugave about his studies. He gives me the answer I'd expect from a college student: he enjoys his classes and is excited about eventually applying the ideas he has encountered at A.U. I dig a little deeper and ask about the effects of the country's farmland redistribution. "With big farms, Zimbabwe used to be the bread-basket of Africa," I say. "Can it happen again, with the three or four hectare plots we're seeing now?" Mugave reflects briefly on logistical problems associated with smallholdings — purchasing small quantities of pesticides, plowing with oxen.... It seems to me, however,

that Mugave is more concerned about the breakup of people than the breakup of land. Along with many of his friends, he worries about a crisis in community values. He tells me that nowadays cooperation can fracture even within extended families, "and such things really did not happen in Zimbabwe." I make no comment, and Mugave is quiet for a moment. Then he retreats to safer ground, to the maxims of ag engineering classrooms. "The efficient use of farm machinery on large tracts of land is crucial for success in modern agriculture," he says.

I recall interviews with dozens of prospective field assistants, back in South Carolina. In Zimbabwe the questions are so much harder. They cut so much deeper, yet for that very reason they interest me so much more. "After you graduate —" I hesitate, then decide to continue "— do you think you can help turn around the farm crisis in Zimbabwe? Do you think you'll be able to make a difference?"

Mugave takes his time. It seems to me that he is weighing an issue of some importance. I look at Ab, who is typing something on his laptop. I turn back toward Mugave, who answers at last. "This is a difficult place in the road, Professor Ferguson, but I tell you that my country will recover. The people will make it happen —" there is a pause, then, "— I will make it happen." My new assistant still smiles, but now he looks directly into my eyes, and I almost wonder who has been interviewing whom.

Although I'd be happy to continue discussing the agricultural future of Zimbabwean society, we need to focus on my primary research mission, which involves understanding the current gold mining activity on the southern half of the Africa University campus. Our first task will be to revisit the subsistence miners across the Mutare River, so after maybe 20 minutes of conversation, we leave the office and head south. As we retrace the path I'd taken with G.R. and Ab on Day 1, Mugave tells me he is familiar with the area but has not been there since the recent mining activities began. I remind him that any familiarity is good, and I lay out for him our interview strategy.

"We'll begin with your explaining, in Shona, that we are writing a book about the A.U. campus," I say, "and that we need to learn about gold mining. If I were a miner, I'd be suspicious, so try to convince them that we want to hear their stories, not steal their gold."

I tell Mugave that he should use his own intuition to shape the interviews. "It would great if you can get the miners to speak some English, but if they want to stay with Shona, that'll be OK, and you'll be in charge. Just remember, everybody has an interesting story, and if you ask 'em just right, they'll tell it." Mugave nods, "I think I know what to say. I might even know a few of the miners, and like you said, familiarity is good."

While we work our way up the switchbacks, toward the site where I'd seen the miners on Day 1, the sharp ring of picks and hammers echoes down the valley. Within about a hundred meters of the worksite, we hear voices, and when we round a bend, we encounter three young men standing beside the trail. From their wet trousers and the dirt smears on their faces, we can tell that two of the men are panners. The third is more smartly dressed and shows no signs of having worked at all. Mugave greets the men in Shona. The panners respond in the same language: "What are you doing? Why are you here? What do you want?" Mugave tries to explain our task. The panners ask, "Do you wish to buy gold?" Mugave tells them that we do not, and the two panners talk rapidly to each other. After a short time Mugave informs me that the men are taking a break and will be glad to talk with us. "I am from the United States and will be here for only a short time," I begin quickly. "Can you tell us a little about yourselves and what you are doing?" Mugave translates smoothly, adding, I think, expressions of Shona politeness.

Thus begins our first interview. We speak primarily with the two panners, while the third man stands a short distance away, saying very little. At first the panners, too, are reticent to talk, but as the interview progresses, Mugave gains their confidence, and they become more comfortable with our questions. After a while I point to my camera and ask if I can take pictures. When the panners answer in the affirmative, I begin to focus and shoot, while Mugave continues a conversation about gold and Zimbabwean economics. Ten minutes later another young man, carrying a pick, appears from up the trail. Like the third man with the panners, this newcomer is nicely dressed, and he's far too clean to have been using his pick. After a brief exchange in Shona, the two clean men join the panners, mugging for

Fig. 1.28: On the road, near Mugave's birthplace, Old Mutare

Two Notes on Vocabulary

1. I am not aware of any adjective that precisely describes the sort of mining that takes place on Africa University's campus. Usually I shall write "subsistence mining," where subsistence is used in the dictionary-sense of, "a means of surviving." And, actually, some folks do seek gold on the A.U. campus so that they can make enough money to stay alive. Other men take up a pick or shovel to tide themselves through periods of unemployment or to supplement inadequate wages from their regular jobs. And, probably, a few men become miners to chase a low-probability dream of riches. In any case, all these folks live at the margins of an ailing economy, and most of them would be in even more desperate straits without the occasional gram of gold. So, subsistence is probably not too far off the mark.

2. I should also explain my use of *panner* and *miner*. A few panners work exclusively in the Mutare's sands and gravels, using river water to sluice away lighter material while the heavier gold collects in the bottom of a literal pan or perhaps a more extensive sluice-channel. All panners, in a sense, are miners, but some writers would reserve the latter term to designate people who work at some distance from sluice-water, digging amid rocks and boulders. Usually, Zimbabwean subsistence miners eventually employ water-sluicing techniques to separate gold. For this purpose they may channel rainwater at the excavation site, or they may carry sand and gravels from a hillside dig site down to the Mutare for sluicing and become, literally, panners. I shall not put a fine point on these distinctions and shall sometimes use the terms interchangeably. I have called our first two informants panners because when we met them they were still wet from panning. But I could just as well call them miners because they work a site on the side of Kenya Hill.

my camera while armed to the teeth with various accoutrements of the subsistence-mining trade (Fig. 1.29). I take three or four posed photographs, and then the two panners indicate that we should talk now because soon they'll need to get back to work. The two clean men nod and wave goodbye, heading downhill toward the Mutare-Nyanga Road, and I wonder about the extent of traffic on our trail through the bush. Mugave and I restart our interview, and as we talk, I grab a few candid photos.

As I snap the digital shots, a verbal picture of our new acquaintances also begins to emerge. Both men have finished high school and have worked previously at various jobs. One had taken soil samples for a pipeline company; the other had been employed at a dairy. Both men had worked on commercial farms, spraying flowers. These jobs

(and others) had either ended or else no longer paid a living wage; meanwhile, they say, if a strong man pans long enough and hard enough along the Mutare River, then he can at least stay alive.

Eventually Mugave asks our informants to talk about other panners and miners they know. We are told that many gold hunters are local and have worked in the general area for over 10 years; other diggers and sluicers are more recent arrivals, some coming from 20-100+ kilometers away. In this Kenya Hill area, as national economic conditions have deteriorated, increasing numbers of less-experienced locals, who see mining as one of the few options for eking out a livelihood, have appeared on the scene. Some individuals apparently show up, find a partner, and dig for a single day (or even less). Maybe they feel lucky or bored, like the traveler who ducks into a casino to play a slot machine until his pocket change is gone.

Many serious miners itinerate (that's a good Methodist-preacher verb!), moving from mine to mine when word comes that somebody has made a gold strike. Mostly, we're told, the news travels by word of mouth, and I think briefly about Jimmy Buffett's coconut telegraph and about the Forty-Niners' mobile frenzies in California. Furthermore, the living arrangements of the itinerants remind me of North America's gold-camp squalor. Although the locals typically stay in their modest houses, most miners from outside the region sleep in river-bank dugouts or under sheet plastic lean-tos.

As our interview continues, Mugave and I learn that our two miners are longtime friends who work together as a team (Fig. 1.30). Other panners also work in pairs or in small teams of three to five people. The groups, we're told, are not hierarchical, so everybody "is his own boss." Strangers are generally unwelcome in a mining area, and an itinerant must usually know somebody who is already on site before he is allowed to dig. Conflicts can occur but are said to be rare. Each miner is expected to dig exclusively within his own area, which will be defined informally but with some precision. "If you find something in someone else's area," we are told, "then you are a dead man." Mugave and I do not inquire whether the statement might be meant metaphorically.

Fig. 1.30: Miners taking a break from panning

Fig. 1.29: Miners and friends

Fig. 1.31: A value judgement: gold nugget on $10,000 Zimbabwe bill

Fig. 1.32: Can you guess which man is the buyer?

By now our interview is going well, sometimes in English, sometimes in Shona. Where necessary, Mugave translates, almost unobtrusively, and I am usually able to follow the flow of a real conversation. I ask about the vertical shafts, down by the river. "Ah, some panners dig in the bed of the river, and yes, we were down there too, but we preferred to dig up on the terrace a little. We quit working the shafts about a month ago. It was no longer profitable, so we moved up here on the slope." I ask the how the shafts were dug. Our informants describe how one person would dig while another hauled the dirt up and away. The partners would dig vertically for as much as a dozen meters. When they hit the base of the alluvium, or the "pay zone," they would follow this interface horizontally for up to 15 meters, until the zone played out or the shaft became entirely unsafe. At this point I ask the question that has troubled me since Day 1 in Zimbabwe: "How often do miners die in the shafts?" "A few every year," is the answer.

Near the end of our hour-long interview, when we are discussing the amount of gold that miners find, I ask, "Have you got any gold that you could show us?" After a short pause and an exchange of glances between the mining partners, one informant reaches way down into a pants pocket and extracts a crumpled Zimbabwe $10,000 bill. The panner looks again to left and right; then carefully he unfolds the bill to reveal the tiny nugget of gold it conceals (Fig. 1.31). The irony of this display is not lost to me: something precious is hidden in something with no value at all. Now our informant explains, "This gold weighs about a point, and I can sell it to a buyer in Mutare for 2 to 2.5 million Zim-dollars." He indicates that the value of gold keeps pace with Zimbabwe's inflation because international gold prices are tied to the American dollar. Mugave and I inquire next about the buyers. Our informants indicate that these people visit the digs briefly, on a regular basis, generally during the mornings, occasionally on a late afternoon. If a panner has found a gram or two of gold, he slips away from his dig to conduct business privately. Many buyers work the A.U.-Old Mutare area, and seldom does the same buyer return to the same dig.

As our interviews draw to a close, Mugave and I share a bag of South Carolina peanuts with our new friends. Mugave thanks the

men for their time, and soon we'll be on our way to the main excavation site. But before we leave, I ask whether they would introduce us to some of the other miners. Again the two men exchange glances; then they tell us no.

Leaving the two panners to complete their break in peace, we head on up the Kenya Hill trail. We crest a rise; there's the excavation site — and I stop short, unprepared for what I see. Mugave shakes his head. "You told me they'd cleared 50 square meters; you said five or six miners!" Nodding, I stare in amazement. During the two days since I'd last visited, the miners have tripled the extent of their operation and quadrupled the size of their working party. "It looks like we've got us more of a job than I'd originally thought," I say.

As we'd hoped, Mugave recognizes a few of the miners. They exchange greetings, after which we explain who we are and why we're here. This information evokes a range of reactions from friendly interest to thinly veiled hostility. To his credit, Mugave thinks fast on his feet, and he soon convinces most of the miners that we are not a threat. At this point I suggest to Mugave that I should just be a tourist for a while, and he successfully negotiates permission for me to take pictures in that role. Soon it becomes clear that my presence is a source of amusement to some of the miners. I don't mind this at all, and I think Mugave agrees that we'll obtain more information (more safely) if I continue to play what I really am — the ignorant white-boy

from America. As before, my digital camera serves as a passport to at least the fringes of an exotic (to me) subculture. A miner has been using a broken rock to clear debris under a dolerite boulder; he stops and strikes a formal pose. I shoot, and everybody gathers around to view the image on my Nikon's LCD screen. Two men seize their picks and feign an assault on a giant boulder; I shoot again. Someone says that a generous man would have brought a hand-held photo printer, and I concede the point. After the initial novelty of a photo session dies down, I am able to get more candid shots, and I try to capture the extent of the mining activity (Fig. 1.33). But I cannot encompass the entire site, even with my zoom lens set to maximum wide-angle. Again, I am amazed at how much has happened here, in just two days.

After about half an hour, the two panners we'd interviewed earlier come up the main trail; with barely perceptible nods they blend into the crowd at the excavation site. Two other men put down their shovels and visit a cook-pot under a small tree. One eats something and returns to work; the other lingers by the fire. I realize that a nicely dressed man, possibly a gold-buyer, has disappeared; I don't know where he's gone or when he left. Mugave calls my attention to several miners who are trudging up a newly hacked path that directly spans the half-kilometer between the Mutare River and this excava-

Fig. 1.33: Panoramic view of pit-mining activities on the A.U. campus

More on the Economics of Gold

A "point" of gold is about one gram. At the time of our interview (December 2007) the international market price for gold was about $25 U.S./gram. Since the currency-exchange rate was about one million Zimbabwe dollars for one U.S. dollar, the miners were receiving at best 10% of the market value for their gold.

During a span of several workdays, miners typically find only a gram or two of gold. They sell this as soon as possible and then enjoy their profits for a few days, during which time they become very popular with their friends. Miners with families use most of their money to buy necessities like rice, cooking oil, and soap. If they are lucky, they may also find corn meal, salt, sugar, and milk in the grocery stores of Mutare. Often, however, serious shopping requires a "midnight run" into Mozambique, where a Shona speaker, even without papers, can usually lay hands on a bargain or two. Miners without families to support will often buy clothes (if available) and beer in Mutare.

A very lucky miner might on one glorious day find five to seven grams of gold. This fortunate fellow would purchase more necessities, and his Mutare-splurge might approach heroic proportions.

tion site. Shirtless, these men carry empty burlap bags, and their trousers are wet to the knees. Now other miners are departing down the new path; across their shoulders they carry sacks that contain maybe 50kg of excavation material, which will be washed at the river in search of gold.

Amidst all this coming and going of men whose names I do not know, I am unable to count exact numbers, but I think that roughly 40 people have worked at this site today. Everybody is busy, and protracted breaks are rare, so I suspect that I'll have little opportunity for further one-on-one interviews. Also, as Mugave and I stand here, unoccupied and staring, I sense a change in the mood of the group; perhaps the novelty of our presence is wearing too thin. I catch Mugave's eye and suggest in a low voice that it might be time to leave. Mugave agrees, so we wave goodbye to the miners and begin our descent back down the ridge.

Along the terraces of the Mutare River, we spend the rest of our morning taking notes, acquiring GPS coordinates, and photographing features of the abandoned Bulldog Mine (Fig. 1.36). We also map some of the deep shafts that penetrate the alluvial sediments (Figs. 1.34-1.35), and I try not to contemplate excessively the fragility of life.

Once we've logged all the data I need from Bulldog Mine, we hurry back to the main campus where the University cafeteria may still be serving lunch. As we walk, Mugave reveals that he's already arranged an afternoon field trip for us. "Professor Abercrombie wanted me to take you across the road to Hartzell Mission," he says, "so we can talk to people whom I know very well. You will learn more about Zimbabwe life in general — and maybe about the search for gold

Fig. 1.34: Gravel and sediment of the Mutare River terrace

Fig. 1.35: Shaft mine dug by panners near the Bulldog Mine

in particular." An anthropologist is always interested in establishing context, and I'm eager to develop some perspective on the observations I've made this morning. So Mugave's plan sounds fine to me. We manage to cross the Mutare River with dry feet (Fig. 1.37), and we even make it to the cafeteria before closing time.

* * *

After a serious lunch of *sadza* and boiled vegetables, Mugave and I walk out the A.U. gate, cross the Nyanga Road, and follow an avenue of towering eucalyptus. We are now on Hartzell Mission's grounds, or Old Mutare. Mugave shows me the sights: the chapel, the high school, the administration building. While he acts as tour guide, I snap pictures. It's late December, so Hartzell is in Christmas/Summer Vacation, and the grounds are peaceful, almost empty. I wonder what the place is like when school is in full session with a thousand or so students going about the business of education. I tell Mugave that I know something about Old Mutare that he does not — that in 1891, even before the founding of the Mission, the first regional Mining

Fig 1.37: Mugave crossing the Mutare River

Fig. 1.36: Mugave with GPS receiver
at Bulldog Mine

Fig. 1.38: The "Chitepos"

Commissioner had his offices right about where we are walking. My young assistant nods noncommittally, so I don't know whether I've told him anything new or not. We keep walking.

Mugave leads me to the house of the "Chitepos" (the name is a pseudonym), the oldest couple that he knows at Hartzell. I am initially surprised when he says that Mr. Chitepo is in his early 70s and his wife is about 65. That doesn't seem old by American standards, but then I remember, current life expectancy in Zimbabwe is 40 years, and the median age is around 17. I remind myself that I must be more aware of context.

The house is modest, comfortable, and reasonably furnished; it could be located anywhere in South Carolina. The Chitepos (Fig. 1.38) also look as if they would fit in back home, and as Mugave makes introductions, I begin to feel at ease. After observing the conventions of African polite conversation, I ask the Chitepos to tell me about themselves and about how "Zimbabwe life" has changed over the past several decades. Mr. Chitepo speaks first. He says he went to trade school shortly after the Second World War and was a bricklayer for over 50 years. He is now retired, and from the vantage of his age, he can see many changes in his country. Mrs. Chitepo has been a primary school teacher since she was 20, and she plans to retire soon if she can afford it. The Chitepos show me photographs that record their family history, and they talk about a peaceful life that began to disintegrate around about eight years ago, when economic conditions started to shift in Zimbabwe. This, I think, is part of the perspective I am seeking.

Since my arrival Mr. Chitepo has treated me like an honored guest, who must see nothing but smiles on the face of his host. But at Mugave's insistence, the man eventually agrees to talk about inflation. "Just today I went to the store," he says, "to buy a blade for my razor. Seventy thousand Zimbabwe dollars for a single razorblade! Such a number is much of my pension. So I ask you, how can I pay to spend seventy thousand Zimbabwe dollars for such a small thing?"

After her husband has spoken, Mrs. Chitepo appears more than willing to talk about healthcare, fuel shortages, and the erosion of community values, "Even though there is a hospital on this mission,

A Conversation About the Geology of Gold

While we had been working amid the shafts and the ruins of Bulldog Mine, Mugave had asked me to tell him about the geology of gold. I replied that precious metals were not my area of academic expertise, but that I'd be glad to share what I remembered from undergrad geology. What follows is an abbreviated transcription of our conversation.

I began by explaining that in Zimbabwe, gold deposits are of two types, called reefs and placers. "Reef gold is associated with quartz veins and shear zones in the greenstone belts. The greenstone rocks are fractured with all sorts of shear lines, and molten quartz has been injected into these seams. If you find a quartz vein, you have a chance to find some gold."

"The miners said they were looking for quartz," Mugave nodded. "But how do the veins get enough gold to be worth looking for?"

"Hot water — or hydrothermal activity associated with igneous intrusions around 2.6 to 2.7 billion years ago," I explained. "Hydrothermal alteration basically involves cooking rocks in their own juices until the gold comes out. Extreme pressures deep in the earth force super-heated water through the pores in rocks. Gold is unbelievably rare in those rocks, but the rocks are full of micro-pores, and everywhere the water goes, it gleans up all the gold in ionic form."

Mugave was skeptical. "Gold ions don't sound like the chemistry I learned at Hartzell."

"I know it's weird," I admitted, "but metals normally inert can become chemically active at extreme temperatures. The water's under millions of pounds of pressure, or it'd be steam."

"Millions of Newtons of pressure," Mugave, the African science student, converted automatically to metric units. "Of course all this takes place deep within the earth."

"Nowhere near the surface," I agreed. "The point is, superheated water gathers up the gold and flows into the veins and shears. Quartz is the last mineral to solidify, and gold-bearing water sort of chases after it, concentrating near iron-rich rocks as the quartz cools."

"I got it," Mugave said. "The water begins to cool in the quartz veins, and the gold precipitates out."

"Not exactly," I said, "but that's pretty close. Anyhow, the geology textbooks talk about hydrothermal gold accretions. But here in Africa, they're mostly called reef deposits. The men up at our excavation site are after them."

"And here, in the alluvium?" Mugave pointed toward the nearest of the vertical shafts that honeycombed this terrace of the river.

"Erosion wears away the greenstone-belt rocks, including the quartz veins. The eroded material is eventually deposited in the streams or their banks. Because the gold is denser than the gravels and sand, it can work its way down low in depositional strata. If that happens, you get a concentrated placer deposit. It's what American gold prospectors call pay dirt...."

"...[T]he African peoples...had produced prospectors and 'geologists' who had a clear idea of where to look for gold and copper in the subsoil. When the European colonialists arrived in the 19th century, they found that virtually all the gold-bearing and copper-bearing strata had been mined previously by Africans – though of course not on the same scale as the Europeans were to achieve with drilling equipment."

How Europe Underdeveloped Africa
Walter Rodney (Howard Univ. Press) 1982

"These are the times that try men's souls."

T. Paine,
23 December 1776

it often has no doctors, and the women who work there no longer have drugs to give you. You have to buy your own drugs at prices we cannot afford — if you can find them. And there is no gas. And even if a neighbor has gas and if you ask him to take your child to hospital, he may tell you no — can you imagine it — tell you no! Perhaps you take your child to hospital in a wheelbarrow? Some people today, they will help only themselves." I listen, I take notes, and I wonder how people like the Chitepos will fare in the next years of the 21st century.

After about an hour we tell the Chitepos goodbye, and Mugave promises he will visit them again before Christmas. Then we walk to the other side of the Hartzell Mission — past houses, the orphanage, the hospital without doctors — to the Mudiwa house, where I meet Mugave's sister, two brothers and two visitors (Fig. 1.40). One of these visitors (not pictured) is "Herbert," who will become our next storyteller. This man has, shall we say, an interest in the merchandising of heavy metals.

Herbert is an intense young man on a mission, which is, specifically, to make a decent living for himself and his loved ones in an economy that currently lacks any stability. "Gold is always of value," he lectures, "but the reasonable objective is not to be involved in the digging of it. I would prefer to secure a position along the chain of trade that transfers gold to richer nations."

In the gold business, it seems, connections are everything. Herbert indicates that he has many acquaintances among the gold panners; they would gladly sell to him. He also knows a few buyers, whom he'd like to by-pass, and he even has the names of Indian families in Mutare who might move Zimbabwe gold into the international stream. "What I really need," he says, "is a set of precision scales so that I can weigh the smallest quantities of gold and serve as an honest broker. That is the way to security, with minimal risk...."

Soon a debate ensues over the nature of security and risk. Herbert emphasizes the stable value of gold in an economy with seven-digit inflation. Others mention desperate men with shovels and shady international dealers who could have served as extras in the American movie, "Blood Diamond." I observe that choosing a vocation in Zimbabwe is a bit different from attending a career fair back home at Wofford College.

Day 4: Of Land and Lifeboats: Past, Present, and Future

Heavy rain fell during the night of Day 3, but by morning the sky has been washed to a blue of heartache intensity, and the sun shines yellow-gold as again I follow the dust road (Fig. 1.39) down by the river to revisit Magician Mine. Accompanying me today is my last, shortest, and wisest informant, John Mark Zihwa (Fig. 1.41). John

Fig. 1.40: Mugave (far right) with his sister, two brothers and a family friend

Mark will become my actor's through-line; by his cues I will learn to make some sense out of the great play that swirls around me in eastern Zimbabwe. Or, in the language of the Internet, Mr. Zihwa has links, and links are what I need.

Fig. 1.41: Mr. John Mark Zihwa
"The gold. Yes, yes, thank you for asking, Sir.
Thank you very much...."

John Mark works in one of Zimbabwe's fastest-growing employment sectors. He is a security guard. On the job John Mark sports a blue uniform and a cap. In case real danger should threaten, he is armed with a small "torch," or flashlight. He wears thick, dark-rimmed glasses and claims to be over 1.5 meters tall, which may be an exaggeration because Ab says he's noticeably shorter than Chris, who is five feet two. When John Mark is not explaining the nature of the universe, he typically wears a smile.

John Mark is in his late 60s, born during the tumultuous years of World War II, when Britain was stripping "Rhodesia" of every movable resource to defeat the Axis Powers. He grew up during the post-war cycles of boom and bust. He survived Ian Smith's white-supremacist regime, the unilateral declaration of independence, the North Korean advisors, the Revolution, and more droughts than he is willing to count. Because of his age and background, John Mark calls every white man "Sir," every white woman "Madam," and salutes a lot. These activities irritate Ab, who is sort of a closet socialist and who gave up saluting when he left the Army. (I tell Ab to lighten up a little; for some people, old habits die hard.) Aside from providing substantial amusement

and offering hard-earned wisdom about women and God, John Mark Zihwa is a veritable fount of information about the history of Euro-commercial gold mining in the Old Mutare area. Therefore, I am glad that I shall be spending Day 4 with him.

By 8 a.m. on this spectacular morning, I sit with John Mark amid the ruins of Magician Mine. I offer him a Ziploc of trail mix. "Thank you very much," he says. He speaks these words so often and with such steady cadence that I imagine him as a short, black Elvis who has maintained into old age the energy and enthusiasm of the "Hound Dog" days. "I want to show you something," I say. I have brought back to Magician the four fragments of earthen vessel that I found here on Day 2. John Mark touches the largest piece with his index finger. "Yes, yes," he nods, "that is the kind that our grandmothers made." He takes the fragment into his hand and tells of grandmothers, of pottery hardened over cow-dung fires, of *sadza* prepared in the presence of old men who had killed lions with spears. And, most fundamentally, he tells of the land, of this African land that graciously gives clay for pottery, nutrients for maize, gold for — he shrugs — "and gold for many things."

I know, of course, that I must ask John Mark about the gold. The question will be risky. I have already learned that when one asks this man a question, one receives an answer that is long and unbroken, like a succession of grandmothers who pass pottery techniques and mitochondria across the millennia. I turn on my tape recorder. I have three hours' worth of cassettes; maybe that will be enough.

The Zihwa connection with this region's gold began in the 1920s, when John Mark's father, who had apprenticed in the mines near Great Zimbabwe, came to work in the Rezende Mines of Manicaland. Shortly after Mr. Zihwa's arrival, he married a woman from Penhalonga and started a family. In 1940 John Mark, the fifth of six children, was born. Throughout the first five years after John Mark's birth, Great Britain was in desperate need of gold to support the economy and technology of total war. "Rhodesian" mining was conducted at a fever pitch, and on the Ngambi Estate alone (the southern half of today's A.U. campus), six commercial mines were in simultaneous operation. Mining was in John Mark's blood from the start. Each day as a child, when he carried his father's lunch into the mines, he also brought with him a boy's eagerness to learn about the manly trade of breaking rocks underground. In 1952, when tuberculosis killed John Mark's father, an uncle appeared at the funeral, prepared to take the Zihwa children back to their father's people in the south. But John Mark's maternal grandmother would not hear of it, and the young boy stayed in Manicaland's mining country.

As soon as he was old enough, John Mark sought employment with Rezende Mining. He was prepared to work underground, but his fluency in English soon secured a better position for him, and for a decade he worked as "manservant" to a succession of mine managers. (His admiration of these men and their families is evident whenever he speaks of them.) In the 1970s, economic conditions in southern Africa began to drive unemployed Malawian and Mozambican miners down "the Free Trade Road" toward the mines of "Rhodesia." Because John Mark had a facility with languages, and because they trusted him, Rezende's managers designated him to be their security guard and interpreter. In these capacities, John Mark would eventually come to Rezende-Redwing's operations at Bulldog and Magician Mines, on what is now the Africa University campus.

While John Mark talks constantly into my tape recorder, the two of us seek more fragments of the earthen vessel from Magician. But after three days of good rains, thick grass covers the ground, and we find nothing. With effort I break into John Mark's narrative and ask him about operations on this specific site. He thanks me twice for the interruption and points to one of the shafts. "I think we cut that one, Sir, but I forget some things, and Rezende did not stay here for long."

John Mark points out a skeleton of twisted metal and a pile of fist-sized steel bearings: "It was the ball-mill that crushed the ore that contained the gold (Fig. 1.42)." He walks me to the concrete cistern where Ab had rescued the toad: "The water was used in cyanide-extraction." He indicates a rectangular outline of stones: "Yes, yes, a garden, thank you very much." I tell John Mark that on this deserted spot, his memories paint me pictures of a different world. "It

Fig. 1.42: John Mark describing the operation of the ball-mill.

was a busy world, Sir. And it was a prosperous world for some people, until it ended." When John Mark says that major commercial operations ceased on this land in the 70s, I tell him that Mugave and I found a claim-marker dated 1991 (Fig. 1.43). This information gives John Mark the excuse to resume his interrupted narrative. "Yes, yes. In the early 1990s, gold panning returned to the Mutare River valley, at first with the sanction of our government, but then...." ["Appendix 2: Disconnected Chronological Notes on the History of Gold in Zimbabwe" outlines the rest of the Zihwa narrative and includes other historical and contemporary information as well.]

After maybe an hour, John Mark asks me to cut off my tape recorder, and we sit for a time on the wall of the old concrete cistern, looking across the Mutare River toward Kenya Hill. "Do you see those boys in that excavation site?" he asks. I indicate that I do; "those boys" have been my major preoccupation for some days now. "Have you noticed how rapidly they extend their diggings?" he continues. Again I nod; I could prove John Mark's point with my digital pictures, but it is unnecessary. "I am an off-duty security guard," John Mark says; "if I were an on-duty security guard, we would have to cross the river so that I could run those boys away or arrest them, thank you very much." John Mark is quiet for almost a full minute; I think that may be a record. Then he asks, "Do you know the unemployment rate in this region?" Actually, I do know; the unemployment rate here is one

Fig. 1.43: 1991 Claim Marker

of those statistics that I have somehow gathered. "Eighty percent," I proudly declare. "Well done, Sir, well done. And do you know what proportion of the men in this region now seek gold, Sir?" I shake my head; I have no idea. "Eighty percent!" John Mark announces triumphantly. "And do you think, Sir, that an off-duty security guard at the good Lord's University should deprive that great unemployed majority of its only employment?" Slowly I shake my head. "Thank you very much, Sir," John

Mark says, "thank you very much."

Where Do We Go from Here?

Just one week after my arrival in Zimbabwe, G.R., Ab, and I are back in the Gray Wolf, headed toward Harare and our flights to the States. Ab makes it clear that he doesn't want to leave, and to some degree we all feel the same. Leaving new friends, whom one could learn to love, is discomforting. And leaving new friends who must confront a rising tide of troubles: that's a recipe for serious guilt. On the long ride we talk about small things — airline schedules, digital cameras, the cost of fuel — but mostly we consider this book that we are pledged to write. "The important point," G.R. says, "is to admit that we don't understand everything about Africa University and yet to communicate the things that we do understand." I nod. Ab says nothing; he is looking back, as if he cannot decide what emotions he is supposed to feel.

* * *

The time is now January of 2009. For one year and one month I have sorted through my notes and my memories of Zimbabwe; I have searched the Internet for information, and I have become a pest to the interlibrary-loan specialists at Wofford College. At this point I am still quite ready to confess ignorance about Africa, but I have also tried to tell you some of the things that I do believe. To understand the current exploitation of A.U.'s campus resources, I eventually developed a one-word Shona vocabulary. The word is *kukorokoza*. Today an ever-growing number of folks in Zimbabwe are being forced to become subsistence gold panners (in Shona they are *makorokoza*, "non-legal prospectors"). They survive by living "life on the margins," which is the literal meaning of *kukorokoza*. A current slang-definition of the word, however, better captures the never-give-up attitude of Zimbabwe's people. Nowadays, *kukorokoza* is often taken to mean "making something out of nothing." And a resilient, creative person living on a crowded lifeboat often struggles to construct necessities out of thin air.

I wrote this geology/mining chapter with *kukorokoza* constantly in mind because the word seems to encapsulate the lifeboat existence of many present-day Zimbabweans. Also, the no-surrender *kukorokoza* spirit is a central theme of our entire book. For example, in the next chapter, Chris and Ab will tell you about *kukorokoza* in the context of our campus' living resources. They will write about firewood, frogs, and francolins; they will ask you to think about the needy people who exploit such resources; they will challenge you to wonder whether the exploitation is sustainable. Then, in the book's final chapter, G.R. will introduce you to the A.U. Farm and its workers, and you will confront *kukorokoza*-type trade-offs in the context of agricultural hopes and fears.

In other words, we four authors hope that you readers derive some sort of fulfillment (be it amusement, enlightenment, intellectual stimulation, or even self-satisfying guilt) from the contemplation of difficult issues like subsistence mining because we're going to hit you with similar conundrums again and again.

Fig. 1.44: Making a living in the mines

Appendix 1: More Geology

The topography around Africa University is ever changing, ever new. But the rocks into which that topography has been carved (and which in large part determine it) are mostly 1.8 to 3.5 billion years old. These ancient rocks underlie what geologists call a craton — a large, identifiable fragment of a continental plate that has remained more or less intact for at least a billion years. Cratons may be considered the fundamental building blocks of continents. Approximately 60% of Zimbabwe is made up by — no surprise — the Zimbabwe Craton, one of the earth's most ancient continental fragments. This piece of real estate and the Kaapvaal Craton, which is directly adjacent to the south, started forming about 3.5 billion years ago and make up the core of southern Africa. The geological region has survived repeated continental collisions and breakups since that time.

The Zimbabwe Craton is composed primarily of gneisses, granitic rocks, and greenstone belts. Gneiss is a metamorphic rock, derived under heat and pressure from pre-existing igneous and sedimentary rocks. Granite is a plutonic igneous rock, formed deep within the earth from molten magma that intrudes upward from even greater depths. Sandwiched between granites and rocks of high metamorphic grade (usually gneiss), greenstone belts are elongated geologic features of low to medium metamorphic grade. These belts are typically made from a variety of mafic and ultramafic igneous volcanic rocks. (Remember the narrative in the text about volcanic ash and rock falling into oceanic sediments; remember that these sediments are subjected to tectonic metamorphosis and uplift.) The presence of inculcated iron and magnesium, often expressed as chlorite, gives greenstone belts their characteristic color. Many greenstone belts contain important mineral resources, including base metals and gold, a significant fact for Africa University.

The Odzi-Mutare-Manica Greenstone Belt (OMMGB, Fig. 1.46) is located in the eastern portion of the Zimbabwe Craton and is approximately 2.7 billion years old. From the Save River in the west, this belt trends east-northeast for approximately 250 kilometers, passing through Odzi and running north of Mutare into Mozambique, where it ends about 40 kilometers northeast of *Cidade* Manica. The OMMGB is geologically complex. Surrounded by the oldest rocks of the craton (mostly gneisses, aged > 2.8 billion years), the belt's margins are primarily metamorphosed mafic and ultramafic volcanic rocks, which also underlie the belt's center. By contrast, the center per se is composed mostly of metamorphosed sedimentary rocks. If that weren't complicated enough, about 2.7 and again around 2.6 billion years ago the OMMGB and the surrounding gneisses were intruded by granitic rocks. Where these hard, granite features have been exposed by erosion, they often form a variety of landforms with strange names such as *kopjes*, whalebacks, and *bronhardts*. Examples of these landforms can be seen in the area surrounding Africa University and along the road to Harrare (Figs. 1.4-1.6).

The Africa University campus is located in the OMMGB (Figs. 1.46-1.47). The alluvial flatlands of the campus' northern half are underlain by granite and associated intrusive igneous rocks such as tonalite. By contrast, the campus' mountainous southern half lies atop a zone of erosion-resistant banded-iron formations (Figs. 1.47-1.48) that also involve such rocks as serpentine, greenstone, epidiorite, talc, and actinolite schist. Along the southern edge of campus are bands of conglomerates. These divide older rocks from the younger metamorphosed-sedimentary rocks comprising the center of the OMMGB. In the southern portion of campus, the youngest rocks (aged just over 1.8 billion years) are dolorites (Fig. 1.49). These have intruded into and cross-cut all the other rocks of the greenstone belt. Also, dolorites make up the backbone of Kenya Hill — and therefore of the boulder field where we observed so much subsistence mining.

Fig. 1.45: Composite of 1970s topographic map and 1990s aerial photograph of the Woodlands and Ngambi Estate, which became Africa University (outlined in gold)

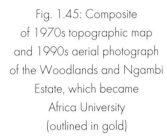

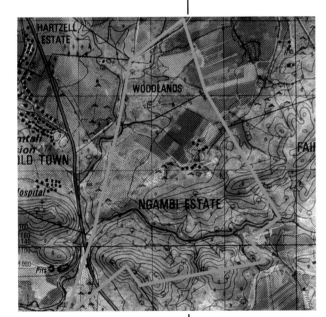

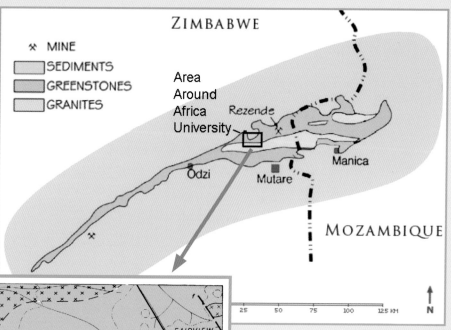

Fig. 1.46: Odzi-Mutare-Manica Greenstone Belt (adapted from Forster et. al. 1996)

GEOLOGY OF THE SOUTHERN AFRICA UNIVERSITY CAMPUS

SCALE OF YARDS

1000   500   0   1000   2000

DOLERITE   GRANITE AND TONALITE   METASEDIMENTARY ROCKS
CONGLOMERATE BAND   SERPENTINE TALC- AND ACTINOLITE-SCHISTS
BANDED-IRON-FORMATION   GREENSTONE AND EPIDIORITE
MINE   f — — f   FAULT   · · · · ·   TELEPHONE LINE   ···· CONTOURS

Fig. 1.47: Map of geology of the southern A.U. campus (Adapted from Phaup 1937)

Fig. 1.48: Cobble from banded-iron formation showing alternating bands of quartz and iron minerals

Fig, 1.49: Dolorite showing oxidized outer surface and dark iron and magnesium-rich, unweathered interior

Appendix 2: Disconnected Chronological Notes on the History of Gold in Zimbabwe

- In prehistoric times local artisans used Zimbabwean gold mostly for jewelry and other ornamentation, but for the past thousand years, little of Zimbabwe's gold has stayed in-country.

- By the 11th century, Arab traders were moving the precious metal eastward to the Indian Ocean and up the coast of Africa to Zanzibar.

- During the 1500s, Portuguese adventurers became involved, diverting much of the gold's flow into Europe.

- In the 19th and early 20th centuries, the British transferred Zimbabwean gold through South Africa to London and the markets of Europe.

- After World War II, a succession of European and South African companies mined the land we now call Africa University. Their claim posts can still be seen today.

- In 1992 gold panning along streams in Zimbabwe was legalized and actively encouraged, with the stipulation that permits were obtained and that all gold was deposited with the Reserve Bank or its agents. Mitigation of environmental damage (chiefly by backfilling) was also required and was monitored by regular inspection.

- After the launch of Operation Chikorokoza Chapera ("No Illegal Panning") in November 2006, subsistence mining operations of the type we observed became unlawful. During 2007, at least two police raids occurred in the area around Africa University.

- In the latter part of 2008, for various reasons (hyperinflation prominent among them), commercial gold mining operations that had been profitable for many years began to disintegrate.

- In October, 2008, the industry recorded a 64% decline, with production of only 125kg, "an all-time low" according to the national Chamber of Mines.

- In November, 2008, South African-owned Metallon, one of the regional giants, closed its five mines. Apparently, the final straw for many mines was non-payment for gold delivered to Fidelity Printers & Refiners, a subsidiary of the Reserve Bank of Zimbabwe.

- At the same time (November-December 2008), Russian commercial mining firms expressed an interest in the gold on the A.U. campus and attempted negotiations with University leadership.

- Today, most subsistence mining at A.U. is probably non-legal, and its ecological impacts are not mitigated. Numerous shafts remain open. During rainy seasons they can become overgrown and/or partially collapse. Thus they become hazards to people and wildlife.

- At the time of this writing, the status of properly filed, pre-University claims on A.U.'s campus is ambiguous. I have been told that some gold buyers might be working for previously permitted claim owners; if so, then technically, some of the current subsistence mining may be lawful. Legal aspects of mining at A.U. are beyond the scope of this preliminary investigation.

Appendix 3: Ecological/Moral Dilemmas about Mining

The future of mining on the Africa University campus poses numerous moral dilemmas. Should commercial mining operations resume, perhaps even under Russian control? We are confident that this time the mining operations will not be allowed to extract gold by the use of mercury, thank you very much. Still, Russian mining corporations do not have enviable environmental records in the other poor countries that they have invaded. Near Africa University, an expected denuding of the land for massive surface mines will destroy significant habitat, and the consequent siltation of the Mutare River will impact water availability for human consumption as well as for agriculture and wildlife. Furthermore, our (admittedly limited) experience with gold-mining operations has not convinced us that cyanide-extraction procedures, like those the Russians generally use, are always safe. Indeed, to some degree they are inevitably damaging, ecologically. Under the best conditions, the resumption of Euro-mining could bring badly needed capital into eastern Zimbabwe, and Zimbabweans might be justly compensated for their land and labor. But deep down we fear yet another case of Europe's "underdeveloping" Africa.

An alternative mining model, of course, involves operations like those we observed at A.U., where shirtless men dig amid boulders with picks and crowbars (Fig. 1.50). We consider such work admirable, even heroic. Indeed, few activities illustrate the unconquerable Zimbabwean spirit of *kukorokoza* — the making of something out of nothing — better than subsistence mining. Still, we must be careful not to romanticize the enterprise. It is marginally legal, at best. It is extremely dangerous. In exchange for backbreaking labor it provides rewards that

Fig. 1.50: *Kukorokoza*

are almost inevitably small — and are so unpredictable that a stable family life cannot be supported by their systematic accumulation. And the merchants of gold, those who profit most from the enterprise, contribute minimally to their nation and to those laborers who do the real work. These small-scale mining operations also have deleterious environmental consequences. The increased scale of the Kenya Hill mining activities discussed in this chapter, for example, resulted in the removal of a great deal of vegetation. The exposed land surface has been carved so steeply that the risk of landslides has been exacerbated.

Mining of this type will also increase erosion, which, coupled with the direct input of suspendable materials by panning, will adversely affect water quality in the Mutare River. Obviously, substantial additional expansion of the excavation site will have substantially increased impact.

Through observation, study, and discussion, your four authors have worked to obtain clarity about these and other issues associated with campus gold mining. Regretfully, however, our sacks full of dirt-and-gravel knowledge have not yielded any bright nuggets of wisdom. (Sometimes, things just don't pan out!) Therefore, instead of guidance, the most we can offer to friends of Africa University will be four insights that are easier to write down than to act upon.

FIRST, supporters of Africa University should be thankful and proud that the A.U. campus provides subsistence-livelihoods for people who are driven underground — literally and figuratively — by a mix of hope and desperation.

SECOND, long-term human and environmental cost-benefit ratios of both commercial and subsistence mining are unknown. And A.U. will eventually need some sort of reasonable estimates.

THIRD, issues surrounding subsistence and commercial mining are complex, with geologic, historic, environmental, political, economic, legal, and ethical dimensions. Nevertheless, University-level decisions about those issues should be made deliberately rather than by default.

FOURTH, such decisions should consider the long-term welfare of the University, of the land and its biota, of the broader community, and of the individuals who currently depend upon the land for their subsistence. Fortunately, University decision-makers can call upon the academic insights of a multi-faculty institution and upon the charity of the church that supports it.

Appendix 4: Suggested Readings

If you are interested in learning more about the land and people of eastern Zimbabwe, here are a few suggested readings:

Forster, H., F. Koenemann, and U. Knittel. 1996. "Regional framework for gold deposits of the Odzi-Mutare-Manica greenstone belt, Zimbabwe-Mozambique." *Trans. Instn. Min. Metall. (Sect. B: Appl. Earth Sci.)*, 105:B66-B73.

McCarthy, T. and B. Rubidge, 2005. *The Story of the Earth and Life: A Southern African Perspective on a 4.6 Billion-Year Journey*. Struik, Cape Town RSA.

Phaup, A. E. 1937. "The geology of the Umtali gold belt." *Bull Geol. Surv. Sth. Rhodesia*, 32.

Phimister, I. 1974. "Alluvial gold mining and trade in nineteenth-century south central Africa." *Jour. of African History* XV, 3:445-456.

Sayce, K. 1987. *Tabex Encyclopedia Zimbabwe*. Quest Publishing, Harare, Zimbabwe.

Fig.1.51: Subsistence mining amid the trees: Kenya Hill, December 2007

creatures

chapter two

"There is a grandeur in this view of life, with its several powers having been originally breathed by the Creator into a few forms or into one; and that, whilst this planet has gone cycling on according to the fixed laws of gravity, from so simple a beginning endless forms most wonderful and most beautiful have been, and are being evolved."

Charles Darwin

"He formed the creatures at his word,
And then pronounced them good."

Isaac Watts

Ten thousand years ago a traveler in North America or Europe could, in appropriate habitat, observe elephant, giraffe, rhinoceros, and a host of other large mammals that characterized the landscapes in which our own species came of age. But the world changed: human exploitation, shifts in climate, and the development of agriculture caused the extinction of the Pleistocene megafauna throughout the northern latitudes. Today, to glimpse a native elephant in the Northern World, one must search fossil beds, museums, or the smoked walls of ancient caves.

The Pleistocene still lingers in southern Africa, but increasingly its large mammals are restricted to National Parks and game reserves. In the region of Africa University, elephants were extirpated over a century ago. Giraffe have vanished too, and a wild rhinoceros would raise as much astonishment along the Mutare River as it would along the Mississippi or the Danube.

Maintaining large mammals in the wild is a costly enterprise, and conservation biologists have strategized for decades about how nations in the developing world can afford to preserve viable populations of these extraordinary creatures. The plight of Africa's large vertebrates is a critical concern for conservationists, but our present purpose is not to expand the already voluminous literature on that subject. Instead, the aims of our book's "Creatures" chapter are more modest. Nevertheless, we believe them to be equally important and exciting.

The authors of this volume grew up in American places not too different from Mutare, at

intersections between small towns, agriculture, and urban sprawl. Tromping through our local woodlots, swamps, and windrows, we discovered joy in this mosaic landscape, and our free days would find us with field guide and notebook (or, for the real rednecks among us, with fishing pole or .22 rifle), scouring our wild world for interesting critters. The instruction of our high school science teachers and the precepts of our churches convinced us intellectually that the natural world was worthy of our concern. And our days afield captured our hearts, proving at a visceral level the transcendent importance of living things. So we became committed to the stewardship of modest wildlands. And if the landscapes of our childhood could not offer eland or elephant, they did give us cottontail rabbits, cottonmouth moccasins, and an occasional rattlesnake. For Ab and G.R. and Terry and Chris, this was grace sufficient.

With an area of about 600 hectares, Africa University's campus is tiny by the standards of National Parks and other officially protected areas. Also, about 10% of the campus is covered by the usual dormitories, parking lots, playing fields, and academic buildings. And another 10-15% is occupied by the A.U. Farm, which will be the subject of the next chapter. But still, by our childhood standards, the residual land (if you like English units, call it a thousand acres) is a vast and wonderful wilderness. Furthermore, for at least four reasons, the University campus may have conservation significance substantially greater than the value suggested by its mere size.

First, as you learned in our geoarchaeology chapter, the landscapes of Africa University are diverse. In addition to the A.U. Farm and the infrastructure of a conventional college, the campus includes flatlands, hills, valleys, woodlands, ephemeral and perennial wetlands, successional fields, and a largely unobstructed run of the Mutare River.

Fig. 2.1: Flap-Necked Chameleon

Fig. 2.2: A.U. Lowlands

Fig. 2.3: Lawn in front of Ag Building

Fig. 2.4: Harvesting wheat, A.U. Farm

Second, Africa University is a habitat-island within a patchwork of maize plots, wheat fields, wooded hills, and rangelands. It is perhaps the largest among several such habitat-islands, and it is probably the best protected. Furthermore, the foothill mosaic of Mutare and Mutasa Districts is nestled in the shadow of the Eastern Highlands, a sparsely populated spine of mountains that straddle the border between Zimbabwe and Mozambique. By preserving remnants of undeveloped flatland, "islands" like Africa University substantially augment the more extensive mountain habitat. The idea, of course, is that a more varied landscape will shelter a more diverse biota, that mountains with even a pinch of flatlands can sustain more species than mountains alone. This presupposes the existence of "connections" between habitat types, and later in this chapter we shall emphasize the importance of connective corridors.

Third, the University's Faculty of Agriculture and Natural Resources includes students and teachers with the inclination and expertise required to investigate scientifically various strategies by which the University's lands could be managed. Furthermore, the commitment of the Agriculture Faculty is not transient but will continue long after the findings related in this book have been superseded by continuing research.

Finally, Africa University and its associated wildlands are under the charge of the United Methodist Church, an institution doctrinally committed to the exploration of just and sustainable patterns for stewardship.

Organizational Plan

This chapter does not present a formal survey of Africa University's biodiversity. We have had scant logistical resources at our disposal, and our time afield has been limited to a few thousand person-hours. Furthermore, we are not trained taxonomists, and at A.U. we have encountered some organisms (particularly plants and orthopteran insects) that motivated us to shout, "What the heck is this?" Nevertheless, our photographs will show you a sample of the University's biodiversity, biased by the luck of our fieldwork and by our particular fascination with vertebrates. And our text will explicate the natural history of some species depicted in our photographs.

We have organized this chapter around the taxonomy of the animals that inhabit the Africa University campus, but we have retained the liberty to skip around a little and to include habitat-related photographs of associated plants and landforms where appropriate. We recognize from the outset that our creature coverage is uneven, and where it is particularly slim, we may impose a pretty sunrise, sunset, or flower picture, just to keep you turning the pages. We have resisted the temptation to include off-campus photographs of on-campus species. For example, although leopards supposedly vanished from our area around the time of World War II, we discovered in September of 2000 that at least one of the cats occasionally skirted across the edges of the campus. We have, over the years, managed to take leopard photographs in various zoos and National Parks. However, it would demean the intelligence of the A.U. stealth-leopard to present other cats' photos in what purports to be a campus viewbook!

We have also decided, reluctantly, to exclude photographs of off-campus University activities. For example, in October of 2007, our Wildlife Management students took a three-day fieldtrip to Mana Pools National Park, where we worked among the buffalo and elephants. Our students made some fabulous photographs (we will share one with you in the "Partnerships" section of this book), and we could have included them in this chapter. But we resisted the temptation; if you want to see African megafauna pictures, we can recommend excellent books and websites devoted to that purpose. As explained in our Introduction, this is supposed to be a campus viewbook, and that is what it shall remain.

We shall begin our creatures survey by writing about invertebrates, entirely neglecting microorganisms and giving only minimal attention to spiders, snails, centipedes, millipedes, and crabs. We won't tell you much about insects either, but termites are so interesting and so important that we devote two pages (pp. 58-59) to their consideration.

We'll initiate our vertebrate section with fish, but we'll show only one species and then move on to amphibians. We are fascinated by frogs — by their abundance, by their diversity, by their colors, and by their songs. We shall explain briefly the reasons for our fascination, and then we'll tour you through a selection of perhaps a dozen species.

After we discuss frogs, we shall turn our attention to the Amniota, a magnificent group of vertebrates comprised by all species that protect their developing embryos with special extra-embryonic membranes. These are the mammals, birds, and reptiles.

The synapsids, ancestors of mammals, were the first group to diverge from the central amniote tree (at perhaps 310 million years before the present). Also, for many American visitors, mammals are the ultimate expression of all things wild in Africa. For these two reasons we'll begin the Amniotes Section of this chapter with a discussion of porcupines, pangolins, genets, antelopes, and so forth. We also shall remind you about the big, hairy, intelligent bushpigs, a species whose status we considered in the Introduction of this book.

Our reptiles section begins in praise of hingeback tortoises. This is in part because we are taxonomic traditionalists, who still believe that turtles were the first group to diverge from the reptilian general evolutionary lineage. At least that's our excuse for giving chelonians priority of place. Actually, Chris and Ab just like turtles so much that we can't wait to write about the critters.

Arthropods

The Arthropoda, or the Jointed-Legged Ones, is by far the largest phylum of living creatures. On the A.U. campus it is represented by spiders, scorpions, millipedes, centipedes, crustaceans, insects, etc.

Fig. 2.5: Spider at night

Fig. 2.6: *Potamon perlatus,* Common River Crab

This crustacean is abundant in all A.U.'s flowing water and is the dominant component in the diet of the campus' Small-Clawed Otters.

Millipedes. These arthropods subsist largely on detritus. They have two pairs of legs per body segment (the predaceous centipedes have only one). The most familiar A.U. myriapods are Giant Millipedes of the Family Spirostreptidae.

Fig. 2.7: Millipede and bug-predator

Archosaurs are the next branch on the Tree of Life. And because the A.U. campus has no crocodiles, we'll limit our discussion of archosaurian "reptiles" to birds. Although we don't have many pictures of these modern, feathered dinosaurs, we shall show you a few and declaim briefly on the diversity of Africa University's avian fauna.

Then we'll offer you a few words about lizards and snakes, and we shall conclude this Creatures chapter with two pages (pp. 92-93) about our experiences with on-campus pythons.

In the accounts that follow, we introduce new taxonomic categories with general statements (set off by font and sometimes color), and, if possible, we illustrate species accounts with photographs.

Invertebrates: Creatures without Backbones

The vast majority of the world's animals are in this category, but we shall consider fewer than a dozen: a millipede, a centipede, a few insects, and a snail.

In wintertime, when the cold nights of July make you snuggle under two blankets and an occasional morning can be etched with frost, you won't see many invertebrates abroad on the A.U. campus. But if October heat brings November rains, the land will come alive. Millipedes are among the most abundant of the animals that reappear

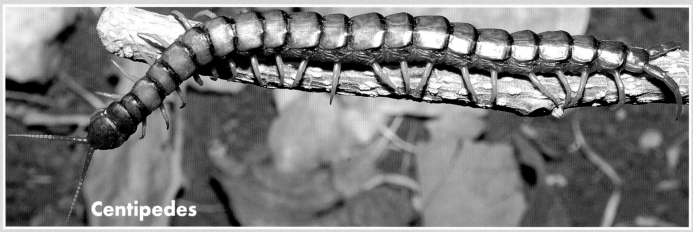

Centipedes

Fig. 2.8: *Scolopendra* centipede

These arthropods have one pair of legs on each of their many body segments. Typically fast-moving, they are abundant, active hunter-killers. Unlike insects, centipedes have no waxy cuticle to waterproof their exoskeletons, and therefore they can dehydrate rapidly in dry air. In part for this reason, centipedes spend most of their time under cover and are seldom seen abroad except at night.

We have observed relatively few centipede species at Africa University, but one of them has been an impressive *Scolopendra* that approaches 20cm in length. (The species is probably *S. attensi* but we don't really know our centipedes, and *S. zuluana* is another possibility.) *Scolopendra* is an ancient genus with about 85 species, and its distribution across all continents (except Antarctica) suggests an evolutionary origin antedating the dinosaurs. Like all other centipedes, *Scolopendra* is venomous, delivering its poison through two highly modified "legs" (called maxillipeds) on the first body-segment. Although this centipede is not dangerous to people, its bite/sting is painful and may motivate the use of language unacceptable in A.U.'s polite society.

in springtime. And although Manicaland is blessed with a multitude of myriapodan species, if somebody at A.U. says "millipede" to you, she or he probably means a giant, black invertebrate of the genus *Archispirostreptus* (we are not certain about the species) (Fig. 2.10). From under rocks and logs, from the stumps of fallen eucalyptus, from beneath the ground itself, these 12cm giants appear in legions. As harmless detritivores, they feast

Fig. 2.9: Dragonfly (*Anax* sp.)

eggs until they hatch ("guarding" is probably too strong a word) though she shows no long-term attachment to the offspring.

Giant millipedes, of course, are entirely innocuous (though do not try to eat one!), and small children sometimes amuse themselves by collecting millipedes and even racing them. Furthermore, for any springtime visitor to Africa University, giant millipedes are a memorable feature of the landscape. The

Fig. 2.10: *Archispirostreptus* Giant Millipede

Fig. 2.11: *Archispirostreptus* mating

on decomposing biota. Rotting grass, broken mushrooms, or road-killed snails: all are fodder for a hungry millipede. And after the first rains, this animal is so abundant that only a careful pedestrian can walk from A.U.'s chapel to the Ag Building without committing mass millipede-i-cide.

Meanwhile, the behavior of African giant millipedes does not focus entirely on food, for in Zimbabwe's spring, the animals' tiny brains are also occupied with thoughts of love — or at least with instinctive patterns of reproductive behavior. A male usually initiates courtship; he approaches a female and walks parallel to her, often with bodies touching. Then, eventually, the female lifts the front of her body slightly to indicate receptivity. The male wraps in a spiral around her, and mating occurs (Fig. 2.11). Shortly thereafter, the female digs back underground and compresses the soil to create a tiny nest chamber in which she may lay hundreds of eggs. Often she stays with these

sheen of their bodies, as sunshine follows a morning rain, is enough to convert even a vertebrate biologist to the temporary pursuit of myriapodology.

Although extraordinarily abundant in springtime Zimbabwe, giant millipedes have few enemies. If one is actually attacked, its first defensive response is to curl into a tight ball. If further disturbed, the animal will give off an almond-smell. This suggests that *Archispirostreptus*, like most other millipedes, secretes hydrogen cyanide. Scientists are unsure how vertebrate predators avoid this chemical defense, but some birds and at least one species of mongoose seem to manage. A few arthropods are specialized millipede predators, and Fig. 2.7 shows a millipede under attack by a pre-adult instar of a true bug (Order Hemiptera).

Insects

As you can tell from our brief myriapod paragraphs, we'd like to skip forward into our presentation of vertebrates. But there is an obstacle. Metaphorically, we four authors are the lowly foot soldiers of natural history, and the great Class Insecta (Hexapoda) bestrides our route-of-march like a lieutenant general, resplendent with stars, medals, and ribbons. We might like him; we might hate him; we might wish that he would go away. But whatever our views about the lieutenant general, we've absolutely got to slow down and salute. In other words, since over half of all known animals are insects, we need to say a few words about them. We'll show you a beetle and three grasshoppers. Then we'll write at some length about termites.

Fig. 2.12: Armored Cricket (*Bradyporidae*)

Fig. 2.13: *Philematium natalense*, Green Longhorn

Beetles

Near the middle of the last century, Britain's most famous celebrity-biologist, J.B.S. Haldane, was asked what his studies had taught him about the Plan of God. The great man replied that he had detected "an inordinate fondness for beetles." And indeed beetles are gratifyingly abundant on the A.U. campus. They range in size from microscopic to "Oh my gosh!" Some of our favorites belong to the Family Cerambycidae, many of whose members are almost electric-green in color (Fig. 2.13).

Grasshoppers

Our colleagues in the Faculty of Agriculture are generally agreed that Africa University has at least a sufficiency of grasshoppers. This we cannot deny, but we would point out that not all grasshopper species are agricultural pests; in fact a few varieties are economically beneficial. We have not chosen to show any of the more common hoppers; nor do we wish to discuss the Order in any detail. Still, some Zimbabwean orthopterans are so outrageous in appearance that we cannot resist the temptation to offer you a couple of pictures. The first is an armored ground cricket (Fig. 2.12), an omnivore and opportunistic scavenger in a newly established Family largely restricted to Africa and the Arabian Peninsula.

The second is a big Long-Headed Grasshopper, a member of the suborder Caelifera, Family Acrididae (Fig. 2.14). This Family includes the horrifically destructive migratory locusts, but the grasshopper depicted is a member of a different subfamily, the Truxalinae.

We also want you to see a picture (Fig. 2.15) of a really big, scary-looking member of the Tettigoniidae, a Family that also includes the familiar little katydids. This animal just showed up in our office one day, and our African colleagues seemed as surprised by it as we were. Although most orthopterans are plant-eaters, this one is a predator and is probably agriculturally beneficial.

Fig. 2.14: *Acrida* sp., Long-Headed Grasshopper

Fig. 2.15: Orthopteran predator

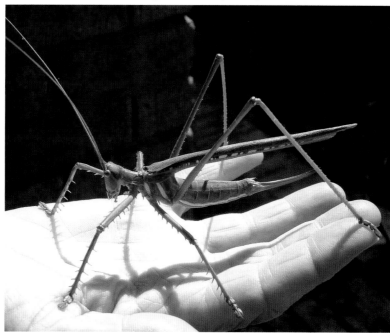

The Construction of Termite Worlds

Fig. 2.16: Termite mound
with escape tower

An American visitor may initially assume that Africa's great herbivores are giraffes, antelopes, zebras, and elephants. In truth, however, more plant calories go into termites than into all these mammals combined. Termites, as we have said, are incredibly common in tropical Africa; in fact, by some estimates they outweigh all the continent's human inhabitants by a factor of 100. In our opinion, the biology of termites merits a long library shelf of books, and although this volume is not the venue for extensive discussion, we can't resist sharing a few insights into the lifeways of these fascinating insects.

Termites, like other advanced animals, cannot produce the enzymes that digest cellulose. And yet they obtain most of their food-energy from dead leaves, dried grass, and even wood. Many termites perform this physiological miracle in roughly the same way that hippos, zebras, and rhinos do — through the action of symbiotic microorganisms in the hindgut that break down the high-energy bonds in cellulose molecules. The great mound-building termites of Africa, however, have evolved a different strategy: they have become agriculturists. Termites of the genus *Macrotermes* chew up bits of wood, dried grass, etc., and they use this pulp as a nutrient-rich substrate in underground fungal gardens that provide their food. This cultivation presents certain difficulties — particularly with respect to oxygen and temperature — that *Macrotermes* addresses through the structure of its mounds.

For optimal growth, the fungal gardens must be maintained at approximately 30-31°C (about 87°F), while the ambient air temperature around the termite mound may vary between the extremes of 0°C and 40°C. Keeping the mound warm is easy. After all, a *Macrotermes* colony typically contains about a million workers plus an even larger biomass of fungi. Taken together, the respiratory activity of all these organisms is substantial. In fact, the net metabolism of a typical *Macrotermes* mound approaches that of an adult human being, and that produces more than enough heat to maintain the warm temperature within the confines of a termite nest. Cooling, however, is a more complex problem, and correct fungus temperatures are maintained only because the entire termite mound is structured as a gigantic respiratory organ.

The typical *Macrotermes* mound is a conical structure that is closed up for most of the year. Air heated by the metabolism of termites and fungi, well below the ground, moves upward within a central chimney. As the warm air rises to the inside-top of the mound, it cools and begins to flow down the sides, back towards the metabolic center of the mound. This heating and cooling tends to drive a buoyancy-circulation of gasses within the mound. The down-flow of air along the porous inner surfaces of the mound's walls would support both thermoregulation and gas exchange (taking in O_2, giving up CO_2). And it might also help maintain optimal humidity levels.

At one time this circulatory process was deemed sufficient to support mound-respiration. Recent studies, however, show that buoyancy differentials within the mound are usually too weak to drive the movement of air with any consistency. And now most entomologists agree that the internal circulation is augmented by the external flow of wind — which, according to Bernoulli's Principle, increases pressure on the

Internal Circulation Model, *Macrotermes* Mound
(schematic cross section)

CO_2

O_2

Center of metabolic achivity

Black arrows indicate internal circulation.

Gas exchange, humidity flow, and thermoregulation occur through the wall of the mound, which is closed but porous.

Fig. 2.17: Termite gas exchange and thermoregulation

windward front of the mound and decreases pressure on the mound's sides and leeward rear. This pressure differential is transmitted through the porous (though closed) surface of the mound.

Wind effects are strongest toward the top of the mound (it's farthest from the ground-surface boundary layer), so gusts tend to augment the upward buoyancy-circulation, while, on the other hand, wind-stills or reversals may temporarily cause air within the mound's central chimney to fall. Because wind speed and direction change very often, the within-mound circulation tends to assume an up-down tidal pattern. Thus, in a sense, the mound as a whole inspires and expires the air surrounding it. Scientists in Zimbabwe have admired "termite air conditioning" for years, and architect Mick Pearce designed the ultramodern Eastgate Building in Harare according to the *Macrotermes* air-circulation principle.

Because much of its structure is sub-surface, a termite mound can provide underground refuge for quite a number of animal species. Millipedes, crickets, and shrews are common residents in open-topped mounds, and in December of 2000, we dug a handsome cobra out of a mound in front of the Ireson-Kurewa Ag Building (Fig. 2.18).

Africa University has many termites, of many species. Some are small and seldom seen, but if you walk northward from the main campus, skirting to the left of the wheat fields, you will enter a savanna-like area where big *Macrotermes* mounds are especially common. During most of the year these mounds may appear inactive, but the termites are always at work. And when summer comes, you can observe *Macrotermes* in all their glory. Even before the rains, as humidity increases, the colony's workers toil through the nights to construct escape-towers above the mound (Fig. 2.16). Then, on a night after the first serious rains, *Macrotermes* mounds will erupt, releasing thousands of winged, sexually capable, males and females. These reproductives, called alates, emerge almost simultaneously from many different mounds and fly in the general direction of some light source, such as a campfire or cloud-shrouded moon glow. Dispersal flights terminate in mating, and newly-paired termites (anthropomorphically termed "kings" and "queens") land, break off their wings, and dig into the ground. There they will start new colonies, which, if things go well, will eventually be complete with monarchs, eggs, larvae, and multiple castes of workers and soldiers.

The mass emergence of African termites is an impressive phenomenon; in some years dispersal flights can be so dense that they darken a sunset sky. Traditional Zimbabweans, however, do not mind, for the alates are large (in *Macrotermes*, about 2cm long) and good to eat. We know that many students and staff at Africa University come from ultramodern subcultures and disparage the consumption of termites. But we have eaten our share of them, and when times were hard, we found a fresh, crisp *Macrotermes* alate to be an acceptable substitute for cashew nuts.

Fig. 2.18: Top: Mr. Kumba with cobra
Bottom: Ab digs; Chris, Mr. Kumba, and Mr. Nzengy'a encourage.

Non-Arthropod Macro-Invertebrates

Snails
Because they are nicely photographable, we shall let snails represent the entire Phylum Molluska — as well as several other phyla of soft-bodied invertebrates commonly known as worms

Like so many other animals of the A.U. campus, snails are seldom seen before the rains of late spring begin. Then they appear in several species, the most striking of which is the East African giant snail, *Achatina fulica* (Fig. 2.19). This is a robust animal, weighing perhaps 250 grams (the largest specimens may approach 1 kg!), with a lovely, veined "foot" that can spread as wide as a man's hand.

Africa University's giant snails, like most other terrestrial gastropods, are hermaphrodites, with each adult possessing both ovaries and testes. Except under extraordinary conditions they do not self-fertilize but, instead, pair off for mating. Courtship consists largely of head-rubbing and typically lasts between 5 and 50 minutes. Mating itself is more protracted, often continuing for more than two hours. If the mating snails are of similar size, each may donate sperm to the other. Otherwise, the larger animal will take the female role. In a single year, a giant snail will lay 5-6 clutches of about 200 eggs each. Egg viability is usually high, and after four or five years' growth, the hatchlings will approach maturity.

East African giant snails will eat nearly any nutritious plant material, and when they are very numerous, they can become serious agricultural pests. On the other hand, they are said to be quite palatable, though we never knew of any people at A.U. who ate them. Birds, mongooses, and baboons prey upon the adults, while some lizards and perhaps a few snakes may eat the juveniles. During the rainy season, smaller snails may be found almost anywhere on campus; we have seen large adults most frequently in rocky outcrops, where the snails may take refuge in cracks and fissures.

Adult *Achatina fulica* are said to make decent (if unresponsive) pets. The USDA, however, prohibits their import into the United States, and snail-smuggling is hardly a worthy enterprise for visitors to Africa University.

Vertebrates

The subphylum Vertebrata (the major division of the Phylum Chordata) includes very roughly 50,000 named species. The majority of these are fish, which are underrepresented in the fauna of southern Africa. Other vertebrates are amphibians, reptiles, birds (which, technically, might be considered reptiles), and mammals.

Fish: The limits of diversity in Southern Africa
Worldwide, fish are the most abundant and speciose of all vertebrates. Zimbabwe, however, is not rich in fish species, and the explanation for this minimal diversity can be found in the biogeography of the Ice Ages. During the cold, glacial times of the Pleistocene Epoch, Africa's enormous size and north-south orientation allowed most species of terrestrial vertebrates to escape the frigid climate by migrating towards the equator. Then, when the climate ameliorated, these creatures could disperse overland back into the regions they had previously inhabited.

On the other hand, the east-west orientation of most southern rivers precluded equatorial retreat by fish, so indigenous species became extinct when southern waters grew frigid and the general hydrology of the region became less hospitable. Therefore, most African fish that survived the Ice Ages were mid-continent tropical types, and

Fig. 2.19: African Giant Snail

almost every fish species found today in Zimbabwe colonized the area from the Congo or the Nile.

On the Africa University campus we have observed, at most, half a dozen fish species. Some, like the ubiquitous African catfishes, are hard-core survivors that can tolerate the thick drying waters of almost any drought. Others, like the Manicaland Barb (Fig. 2.20), are so small that they can find fresh, clear rivulets when larger fish would be left stranded in the congealing mud.

Amphibians: The Fabulous Frogs of Africa University

On an A.U. December evening, when the warm rains of late spring have settled the last of winter's dust and filled the roadside pans with a sheen of standing water, you should put on your raincoat, grab a reliable torch (flashlight), and walk from the academic campus towards the tilapia ponds. If the night is right, you won't go far before you hear, from the middle distance, various chortles and whirrings. The singers are toads — multiple species — and if you like, you might catch a few, to admire their subtle patterns of tans, yellows, and browns.

But don't spend too much time on the toads, for the night will hold other treasures as well. And as you walk the road through the Old Campus, by the farm buildings where A.U.'s first classes were taught, you should hear to your front a cacophony of brief, ascending whistles that have been described as "liquid" or "melodious." These are the calls of Bubbling Kassinas (*Kassina senegalensis*), big-eyed, olive-colored frogs dappled with black and darker greens (Fig. 2.22). To us, the call of kassinas is a quintessentially African sound, as much a signature of the great continent as the cough of a leopard, the trumpet of an elephant, or the *mbira*-melody of a traditional village.

If you continue walking towards the kassinas and approach their fresh-filled pond, you will begin to hear a clicking noise. This is made by Zimbabwe Banana Frogs (*Afrixalis crotalus*), wonderful animals, bright yellow and short as your thumbnail (Fig. 2.23).

The kassinas can be hard to see; they'll be hunkered close to the ground, perhaps under a tuft of grass or at the edge of the water. And

Fig. 2.20: Manicaland Barb

Fig. 2.21: *Bufo gutturalis*, Guttural Toad

Fig. 2.22: *Kassina senegalensis*, Bubbling Kassina

More on the survival of Africa's tropical fish and their dispersal into Holocene Zimbabwe

The drainages of the Congo and (especially) of the Nile extend across the Equator and span many degrees of latitude. Therefore, throughout the Pleistocene's climatic fluctuations, the fish of these river systems could remain within thermally acceptable habitat by dispersing north or south.

After the most recent Ice Age, fish colonization of Zimbabwe occurred mostly through stream-piracy. Young, active drainages leading to the Indian Ocean have back-cut toward the west and northwest, intersecting and "capturing" southern tributaries of older tropical rivers such as the Congo. Thus, Zimbabwe's fishes have equatorial affinities.

Of Frogs and Saints

When we hear frogs call in the African night, we think about one of our heroes, Professor Archie Carr. This man finished college with a Bachelor's in English Literature, but in graduate school he found the "True Religion" and switched to zoology. After sojourns in southern Africa and in the Caribbean, Dr. Carr returned to his native Florida. And over the years he became a patron saint for many Southern herpetologists — partly because he could apprehend nature with amazing insight and partly (we grudgingly admit) because some English teacher had shown him how to write so darn well. Archie Carr loved all things living, but he had a special fondness for turtles and frogs. We think Archie liked turtles because they endure. And he flat-out said that he liked frogs because they know the secret of life, which is to gather with friends on warm, rainy nights, thereupon to sing about the general joy of living and the particular hope of sex.

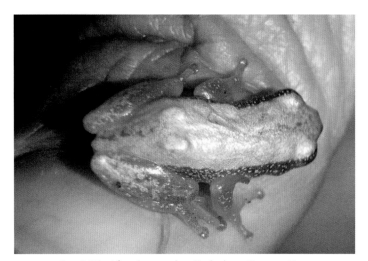

Fig. 2.23: *Afrixalis crotalus,* Zimbabwe Banana Frog

while you're looking for one, you might find a Rubber Frog (*Phrynomantis bifasciatus*), a low-slung shiny animal often tricked out in red and black, like a University of Georgia fan (Figs. 2.32 - 2.34). But you really should keep your eyes open for the Banana Frogs. At first they too may defy your search, but they are irrepressible acrobats, climbing and jumping through low reeds or stems of grass, perhaps 30 or 40 centimeters above the ground. Their movement eventually attracts the eye; we're confident that if you look carefully, you'll definitely see them. And even if you don't see Banana Frogs, you can, for sure, enjoy the A.U. frog-music. It is perhaps the most delightful symphony we have ever heard.

We don't know how many frog species live on the Africa University campus. Presumably the total is between 22 (the number we have observed) and 39 (the maximum that Alan Channing [*Amphibians of Central and Southern Africa*] considers possible for all of Manicaland Province). We do know that A.U.'s anuran fauna is highly diverse: eight Families occur on campus, and that's about the same as in the entire USA, which is a bit bigger than our 600 hectares. Also we know that virtually all species are rain-dependent.

Rain, and frogs, should not be taken for granted in southern Africa. In wintertime, you typically don't see either one, and if you do, the vision is fleeting and pretty much irrelevant. But during September the cold abates, and in October the days are actually warm (you might consider them hot, if you're a Yankee). November — well, November is for Old Mutare the month of Maybe. During November the southward progression of the solar equator gives us more daylight and more direct input of radiant energy that can heat the air and cause it to rise. Rising air, pushed ever higher by warmer air beneath it, begins to cool, and as the air cools to its dewpoint, water vapor within it condenses around the microscopic dust particles always present in Zimbabwe's spring air. When the condensing droplets reach a critical size, they fall to earth as convective precipitation, summer rain, the rain that gives life to Zimbabwe's people and frogs.

As any Zimbabwean can tell you, in some years this miracle does not occur. Moisture-bearing air masses stall in the Equatorial North and fail to cross the Afro-Montane Highlands that shadow us from the Indian Ocean. Obviously, no amount of convective uplift can squeeze water out of dry air, so drought results. During drought years Old Mutare becomes as dry as a bad statistics lecture: maize plants shrivel before they bear, children go hungry, and A.U.'s frogs have nothing decent to sing about. But in a good year, summertime brings the rains to Old Mutare. Maize ripens in bountiful supply. Termites emerge in clouds that excite the palates of laughing children. Pangolin and aardwolf haunt the margins of civilization. Church crowds shout their grateful hosannas. And the frogs of Old Mutare sing with a joy that would delight the heart of Saint Archie Carr.

In an earlier draft of this book, we devoted at least a page to every kind of frog that we had observed on campus, but reviewers with harder hearts (or sounder minds?) convinced us that we should leave some anuran mysteries for you to discover when you visit A.U. So we'll content ourselves with brief descriptions of only 10 species (representing seven families) — though we must show you multiple pictures of some particular favorites.

Family Bufonidae

The toads, or bufonids, are short, chunky insectivores. Most are small to medium in size; most are relatively resistant to desiccation, and most lay prodigious numbers of very small eggs that hatch into tadpoles with low survival-to-maturity rates. Worldwide, this Family has over 400 living species, and the vast majority of them belong to what herpetologists used to call a single genus, *Bufo*. Africa University has at least three *Bufo* species, and we also have a bufonid (Red Toad) that is not a *Bufo*. One might even call it a toad that is not a toad.

Schismaderma carens, Red Toad (Fig. 2.24). Our campus shelters great multitudes of this charming amphibian. Both males and females may grow to a body length of about 90mm. The dorsal color, typically brick-red, is bordered by a distinct glandular ridge running from above the external eardrum (or tympanum) to the rear legs. The skin directly below the ridge may be dark, but the lower sides and belly are lighter in color, and, overall, Reddies appear less warty than most other toads. The advertisement call is a loud whoop usually lasting more than a second. Any rain can elicit breeding, even as early as October. Eggs are deposited in a double string, and because many Reddies may breed in one small puddle, hatchling tadpoles can be quite densely packed. Clutch size is small for a bufonid, averaging "only" about 2500 per female.

Like most toads, *Schismaderma carens* is an adaptable animal, surviving well in agricultural landscapes and other disturbed habitats where it eats countless numbers of potentially destructive insects.

At Africa University we have found Reddies more frequently in the more settled parts of campus, often near or even within academic buildings.

Family Hemisotidae

The hemisotids, or snout-burrowing frogs, are exclusively African, with only one genus and about eight living species. All have pointed, hardened snouts that are used for burrowing.

Hemisus marmoratus, Marbled Snout-Burrowing Frog (Fig. 2.25). Females of this attractive little frog may grow to 55mm, but males are typically less than 35. Most illustrations depict this animal as brown and black, but those we've observed at Africa University were olive-green and gold. The nose is pointed, pupils are vertically elliptical, and a transverse fold of skin may be noted just behind the eyes. A dedicated burrower, this frog usually calls from underground along the muddy edges of small ponds. The advertisement call is a protracted, multi-second buzz that sounds like an insect. During amplexus (mating), as soon as the male clasps the female, she begins to dig forward, pulling the male down into the burrow that she is making.

Fig. 2.25: Marbled Snout-Burrowing Frog

Fig. 2.24: Red Toad

"The whole earth is at rest
and quiet; they break
forth into singing."

Isaiah 14:7

Fig. 2.26: Zimbabwe
Banana Frog singing

After the female deposits her eggs (usually less than 200) and they have been fertilized, she stays with them in a small, underground chamber. If humidity in the chamber remains high, the eggs will soon hatch into tadpoles, which wait in the damp earth for better, wetter days. Eventually, when summer's heavy rains fill a pond to overflowing, the Snoutie's egg chamber floods, and her tadpoles are freed.

At Africa University we have heard this species in several areas, but we have captured specimens only along the edges of partially filled tilapia ponds. Of course we've never actually seen Snout Burrowers outside of their breeding season. Indeed, like most authorities, we guess that these frogs forage exclusively underground. We know some A.U. students with the telemetry skills to test this hypothesis, and wildlife-instrument suppliers build smaller, cheaper radios every year....

Family Hyperoliidae

The hyperoliids, or Reed Frogs, include about 19 genera and 230 living species. These beautiful animals are found throughout tropical Africa as well as São Tome Island, Madagascar, and the Seychelles. All are small or medium in size. Most are brightly colored. And many have the enlarged toepads characteristic of climbing anurans. In our biology lectures we would wax eloquent over hyperoliid toe pads as an example of convergence, the evolution of similar features by unrelated species doing the same ecological job. This Family as a whole has defied easy taxonomic analysis, and the Marbled Reed Frog is particularly problematic for herpetologists who are picky about getting every name exactly right.

Hyperolius marmoratus, Marbled Reed Frog (Figs. 2.27-2.28). We consider this species to be especially lovely, and we devote a full page to photographs of various color-morphs observed at Africa University.

Males are said to reach 43mm in length, but all those we observed at A.U. were smaller. They advertise from reeds and other emergent vegetation in or at the edge of creeks or flooded fields. The call, a brief,

rising whistle, is audible for more than a hundred meters, and research suggests that females select the males that call loudest.

Eggs are glued to sub-surface roots. Females lay multiple, large clutches within a single breeding season. This species (or group of species) occurs through much of non-arid sub-Saharan Africa. At A.U. we have seen and heard this frog most commonly in the thick *Phragmites* reeds that line the campus' lowland creek. This is not an easy area to walk, but Marbled Reed Frogs are worth the trouble!

Afrixalus crotalus, Zimbabwe Banana Frog (Figs. 2.23 and 2.26). This tiny frog is yellow-gold with faint, lighter, lateral stripes.

The advertisement call sounds like a few quick clicks of a rattlesnake's rattle (as the species-name would suggest to a Latin-savvy American herpetologist). Sometimes called a Leaf-Folding Frog, *A. crotalus* deposits its eggs on surface vegetation, folding the leaf and gluing its edges to form a protective envelope. At Africa University we have often found this frog in ponds with Bubbling Kasssinas (see below). Calling Banana Frogs are almost always near the tops of grasses or reeds. Sometimes the tiny males push and shove each other vigorously before mounting the slightly larger females.

Kassina senegalensis, Bubbling Kassina (Figs. 2.22 and 2.29). This is the species whose haunting call we praised at the beginning of the frog-section of the present chapter. Female and male kassinas are of approximately the same size, both reaching about 50mm. Finger- and toe-tips are slightly enlarged. No external eardrum is visible. The dorsal pattern is dominated by a chocolate-brown vertebral stripe that contrasts with a background coloration of tan to yellowish-brown. Additional dark, elongated spots are found more laterally.

As we have written before, the advertisement call is a melodious, ascending whistle that has been likened to the sound of bursting bubbles. Males call from under vegetation, sometimes on land, sometimes at the edge of shallow water. Often males sound off en masse, with several frogs responding to the call of a leader. Although the call is not especially loud, massed choruses can sometimes be heard for well over a kilometer.

Fig. 2.27: Marbled Reed Frog

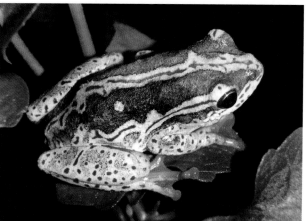

Fig. 2.28: Marbled Reed Frogs

(All are from the same population.)

Fig. 2.29: Bubbling Kassina

Fig. 2.30: Kassinas in amplexus

Fig. 2.31: Mozambique
Rain Frog

A female may approach a male that is calling from dry land — and then, while joined in amplexus (Fig. 2.30), walk/hop with him to the water's edge. Eggs are deposited under shallow water, applied singly or in small groups to rocks, roots, or the pool's substrate.

At Africa University a few of these frogs may begin calling with the very first rains, waiting hopefully along the old canal that runs by the tilapia ponds. Later, as grassland pans begin to fill with water, A.U.'s kassinas start singing in earnest, from multiple locales. And no herpetologist who has heard the call is likely to forget it.

Family Microhylidae

This highly adaptable, cosmopolitan Family is found on every continent except Europe and Antarctica. On Madagascar and New Guinea, microhylids have undergone extensive adaptive radiations, occupying niches usually filled by frogs of other Families (including treefrogs). In Asia, some microhylids are widely foraging terrestrial predators. At Africa University, they are burrowers, frogs to be seen only on special occasions.

Breviceps mossambicus, Mozambique Rain Frog (Fig. 2.31). This is a short-legged, rounded frog, and when harassed, it inflates its lungs to appear almost spherical. The dorsal coloration is variable, ranging from very dark to mottled. A dark stripe usually runs from the eye down to the foreleg. A spade-like tubercle on the hind foot is used to dig rearward into sand or soft earth.

The advertisement call is a very short chip, always rendered from under cover; some local folks believe that it signals the coming of rain, hence the common name. The globular shape of *Breviceps* seems to preclude a conventional, grasping amplexus. The male is much smaller than the female, and apparently the only way he can stay mounted is by gluing himself to the female's back, and he does this by special skin-secretions.

Mating often begins on the ground's surface, and then the female digs backwards to form an underground nesting chamber, often beneath a rock. There she deposits about 20 eggs, which the male (still glued to her back, sometimes for days) fertilizes. The parents then leave the eggs, which eventually hatch into non-feeding tadpoles that "swim" for a few days in the gelatinous egg mass until they metamorphose into tiny froglets.

Members of the genus *Breviceps* are more resistant to drought than most other frogs; if the substrate in which they dig begins to dry completely, they inflate to maximum diameter (possibly to facilitate through-the-skin gas exchange) and secrete a mucus coating that more or less waterproofs the skin.

For us, Rain Frogs have been difficult to find. We have caught only one male; he was under rotting wood atop Africa University's near mountain.

Phrynomantis bifasciatus, Banded Rubber Frog (Fig. 2.32-2.34). Males of this microhylid species grow to a little over 50mm, and females can be about 20% larger. The skin is smooth, and as with many other microhylids, the head is narrow and flattened. The back is black, with two brightly colored lateral stripes typically extending from the snout to the legs. These stripes vary in color from yellow through pink to red and are matched by a sacral spot of the same color. This bright coloration warns potential predators that the frog is quite poisonous. Of course it has no venom (no living amphibian does), and the frog won't bite you anyhow. But if you bite the frog, you will live to regret it — probably. Indeed, although Rubber Frogs are safe to touch, herpetologists with cuts and scrapes on their hands have briefly experienced elevated heart rates, nausea, and breathing difficulties. Furthermore, if you're out collecting frogs at A.U., you should not place this animal into the same container with other anurans; otherwise you'll end up with a bunch of dead frogs.

Through the winter and most of the spring, you probably won't be able to find Rubber Frogs at Africa University. When summer comes, however, *P. bifasciatus* appears as if from nowhere. On rainy nights the species can be observed on almost any road on the A.U. campus.

Rubber Frogs breed in shallow pools, and the advertisement call is a long whirr, often emitted from under cover. This species can hop, but Rubber Frogs are more likely to move by walking or even running.

This makes them difficult for us to photograph except when they are calling (Fig. 2.34).

Family Pipidae

This ancient, primitive Family of tongueless, fully aquatic frogs probably originated on the Gondwana Mega-Continent prior to the separation of South America and Africa; in any case the varmints survive on both of those continents today. For pipids, feeding, breeding, courtship, and calling take place exclusively underwater; in fact, these frogs even lack conventional vocal cords (which are structures adapted for propagating sound through air) and make underwater noises by clicking bony rods in the larynx. In shallow, nutrient-rich waters choked with algae, African pipids employ an unusual survival strategy. They produce numerous tadpoles that eat the algae — and the adults feed in substantial part on their own offspring. This adaptation works well because tadpoles of most frog types are largely algae-eaters, while, on the other hand, no adult frog of any species is capable of digesting any vegetable matter (including algae). In other words, African pipids harvest rich algal blooms indirectly, by consuming their young. This has got to be a metaphor for something!

*X*enopus muelleri, Tropical Platana (Fig. 2.35). Females are large, growing to 90mm, but males, which we have seen more commonly, are noticeably smaller. As the common name suggests, Platanas are quite flat. Entirely aquatic, they have extensively webbed hind feet; the front feet have extremely long fingers, which are used to apprehend the underwater environment by touch. The dorsal coloration is basically gray, with darker blotches visible under some conditions. *X. muelleri* is distinguished from the Common Platana (which is actually less common at Africa University) by having under each eye a tentacle whose length almost equals the eye diameter. The advertisement call (which is difficult to hear above water) is a short, one-frequency click-rattle, emitted underwater.

Although they are restricted to permanent water during the dry season, when the world gets wetter, Tropical Platanas walk/crawl short distances overland to breed in ephemeral pools, where the density of aquatic predators is lower, and where algal blooms may provide ample food for the tadpoles. Transformling platanas move en masse from

Fig. 2.32: *Phrynomantis bifasciatus*, Rubber Frog

Fig. 2.33: Rubber Frog

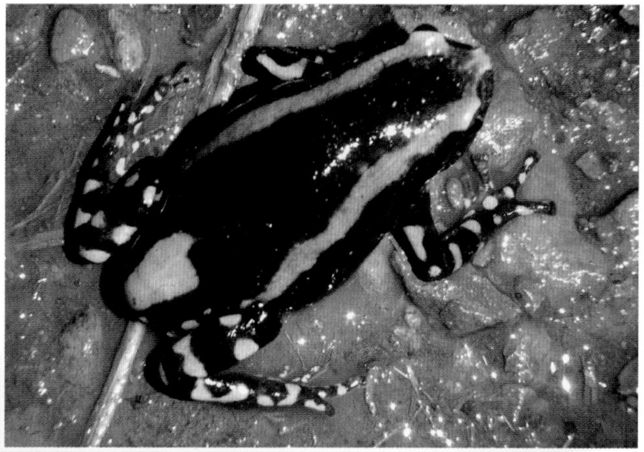

Fig. 2.34: Rubber Frog calling

Fig. 2:35: Tropical Platana

the breeding pools, and although mortality is high, some small percentage of them do find permanent water.

At Africa University, late in the dry season or during the early rains, these frogs may be observed along the edges of partially filled tilapia pools. Usually only their eyes protrude above the surface. Like most fish (and like the tadpoles of some other frogs), adult Platanas have an efficient lateral-line sensory system: they can thereby detect very slight displacements of water, and this makes them a bit difficult to grab by hand. But you should give it a try.

Family Ranidae

This is the biggest, most familiar, and most widespread group of frogs. Eventually herpetologists will split the ranids into several Families, and that's probably a good thing, since the Ranidae as presently constituted includes over 700 species, living on every continent except Antarctica. The ranids best known by most Americans are medium to large frogs, but the Family also includes many small species, particularly in Southeast Asia. Typical ranids are streamlined jumpers living alongside permanent water, but the group exhibits great diversity in body form, habitat, and life history. Most types lay eggs in water and produce conventional tadpoles, but offspring of some African and Asian species develop directly from eggs to miniature froglets. Although frog species can in general be identified by their calls, this exercise is problematic for ranids because a single species in this group may make a variety of noises. Many popular herpetology books label the ranids "Common Frogs," but some species are quite rare, and some are highly unusual, so we would prefer the name "Do-Anything Frogs."

Ptychadena oxyrhynchus, Sharp-Nosed Ridged Frog (Fig. 2.36). The genus *Ptychadena* includes several African species, all called Ridged Frogs because of the distinct longitudinal ridges running in multiples down their backs. Once in hand, the appropriately named Sharp-Nosed Ridged Frog can be distinguished from other members of the genus because the distance from the nostrils to the tip of the snout is greater than the distance between the nostrils. Males are up to about 62mm long, and females may be about 30% longer. The dorsal coloration is typically brown or reddish-brown; the individuals we have seen here also show some green. If you look at this frog from above, you may notice a light-colored triangle between the eyes and the snout.

Males may call at the edge of a permanent pond or from open ground a little distance from the water. The advertisement call is a loud trill lasting about half a second. Frequently these frogs are willing to continue calling even when closely approached, but if you try to grab one of the animals, be prepared for a prodigious leap; the species is said to be the long-distance jumping champion of the anuran world.

About 3000 eggs are laid in a clutch. Although deposited in short strings, they may float apart. At Africa University we have found this species near the tilapia ponds and also along the old irrigation canal.

Fig. 2.36: Sharp-Nosed Ridged Frog

Family Rhacophoridae

Rhacophorids are arboreal animals with enlarged toe pads; they typically breed during heavy rains and deposit their eggs in foam nests constructed over water. Limited to one genus and three species in Africa (with only one species in southern Africa), the Family has radiated more extensively in South, Southeast, and East Asia, where almost 300 species occur. Furthermore, the distribution of these frogs on Madagascar and other islands of the Indian Ocean suggests that ancestral rhacophorids hitched a ride when the Indian Plate broke loose from Africa and moved toward its collision with Asia.

Chiromantis xerampelina, African Gray Treefrog (Fig. 2.37). Males of this species may reach 72mm; females tend to be about 15% larger. The fingers are arranged in opposable pairs and are tipped with large pads. The skin is rough, and the dorsal color is often gray or gray-brown, though coloration of an individual frog may vary a great deal depending on temperature and exposure to light.

Males may call from bushes or trees, in the vicinity of water. As far as we have observed, actual amplexus always takes place in vegetation overhanging a pond that is being filled by heavy rains. The advertisement call is a repeated croak, by which the first "singer" will eventually attract several other males to the potential breeding-tree. If the males keep calling, a female will usually show up, climbing carefully through the branches. One male will grasp the female in amplexus — and then other males may grab onto the breeding couple. (Experiments show that multiple paternity is at least possible, and it may be the rule.)

Meanwhile the female produces a cloacal secretion, which she and the male(s) beat into a foamy froth that will form a protective nest. Often a female will be unable to produce sufficient foam without rehydrating, and her consort(s) will release her so that she can climb down to the pool below and soak up more water through her porous belly-skin. Then she will return to the tree, and amplexus will continue.

Between about 500 and 1000 eggs are deposited in the nest. After amplexus, the outside of the nest will dry, protecting the eggs from desiccation. The eggs hatch into tiny, dark tadpoles that initially rely upon bubbles in the foam for gas exchange. After three to five days, the bottom of the nest softens, and the young fall into the water below where they will eventually transform into froglets. On the Africa University campus, we have most frequently found this frog near ephemeral, tree-edged pools that fill deeply with the first heavy rains. A casual observer is more likely to see the foam nests than the frog itself.

Fig. 2.37: African Gray Treefrog

69

The Amniota: Mammals Plus Birds and Reptiles

These are the animals that protect their developing embryos (whether in eggs or borne alive) with a special set of membranes. Conservative, traditional taxonomists arrange them as indicated in Figure 2.38, below.

In the following pages we shall discuss mammals and then turtles and then birds and then lizards and snakes.

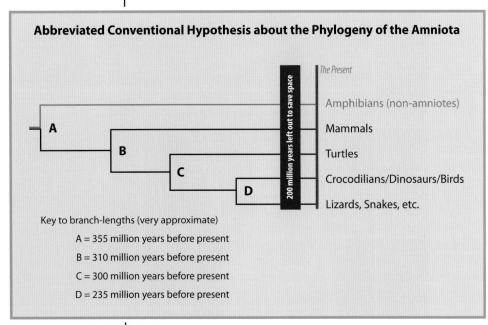

Abbreviated Conventional Hypothesis about the Phylogeny of the Amniota

The Present

Amphibians (non-amniotes)

Mammals

Turtles

Crocodilians/Dinosaurs/Birds

Lizards, Snakes, etc.

200 million years left out to save space

Key to branch-lengths (very approximate)

A = 355 million years before present

B = 310 million years before present

C = 300 million years before present

D = 235 million years before present

Fig. 2.38: Hypothesized branching order
(with very approximate dates)
for amniotes to be discussed in this chapter

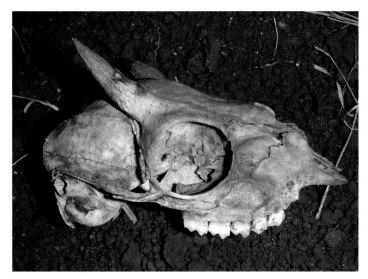

Fig. 2.39: Skull of *Raphicerus sharpei*, Sharpe's Grysbok

Mammals: Campus Diversity in Decline

As we have already suggested, in Africa the word "wildlife" means, predominately, mammals. And certainly any American visitor to Zimbabwe should visit one of the great National Parks to see the vast array of large mammalian species that characterized the Pleistocene world in which *Homo sapiens* evolved.

At Africa University we have expended substantial effort looking for mammals, and we have been able to document the presence of about 35 species on campus (the total does not include people, domestic mammals, or a few rats and bats that we could not identify). The largest of these mammals was a kudu (a spiral-horned antelope weighing over 200kg, observed only once, in 2000); the smallest was a pygmy mouse (*Mus minutoides*, weighing perhaps 5g, also observed only once, in 1993).

So we have not found any elephants or rhinos, but we have been gratified by the diversity of campus mammals — and disturbed by a decline since 1993 in the number of them we observed. Indeed, we used the plight of bushpigs to introduce this book's conservation con-

cerns, and we shall return to this topic after our chapter on farming at Africa University. But for now let us introduce you to the natural history of a few mammalian species that we have observed on campus. Because our photographic coverage of mammals is sparse, we shall not organize these animals in any formalized taxonomic order.

Order Pholidota: Pangolins

Manis temminckii, Cape Pangolin (Fig. 2.40). Nothing else in the world looks much like a pangolin. These animals are fairly large, averaging between 7 and 15kg; they have pointed snouts and elongated bodies. And they are covered with heavy, brown scales.

Although they occasionally taste a few termites, pangolins eat almost entirely ants, which they find during long, nighttime rambles across savannas or low hills. If you see a pangolin on patrol, it will be shuffling slowly along, sometimes walking bipedally, with its front feet held clear of the ground. If you make a quick dash, you can probably catch up with the pangolin, and it will immediately roll into a tight ball, protecting its head and softer underbelly. When you pick the varmint up, however, you should be careful; it will not bite, but if your fingers stick between the sharp-edged scales, you can be badly cut.

Nowadays pangolins appear to be quite scarce in eastern Zimbabwe, but one came strolling through the A.U. campus one night in December of 1993. It was captured, of course, and brought to chapel on Sunday morning. The pangolin was appropriately admired; then, as required by ancient custom, it was donated to the local chief, who ate

it, purportedly in order to obtain increased longevity. (The chief died at a modest age, so in his case the pangolin-charm did not work very well.) Officially, pangolins are legally protected throughout Zimbabwe, and we are told that they are no longer eaten today.

Order Chiroptera: Bats

Among mammals, bats and rodents are the most successful Orders, together comprising well over half of all mammalian species. We have seen quite a few bat species — and hundreds of individuals — at A.U. Many of these bats are associated with the abandoned mineshafts that honeycomb the campus mountains.

Perhaps the most abundant variety has been *Tadarida aegyptiaca,* the Egyptian Free-Tail Bat. This is a very widespread species, occurring from southern Africa through southwest Asia and across the Indian subcontinent.

In Zimbabwe, male Egyptian Free-Tails produce sperm during the late rainy season (perhaps February through June) and retain the sperm in the epididymis until mating takes place, usually in August. This sperm storage is ecologically adaptive because it allows three energetically expensive processes (spermatogenesis, pregnancy, and lactation) to take place during the months when the bats' prey (flying insects) is most abundant.

We are embarrassed that we never took any decent photographs of *T. aegyptiaca,* but Fig. 2.41 shows one hanging at the entrance to its mineshaft, and Fig. 2.42 shows five of them (you have to look very closely) emerging for a night's foraging.

Fig. 2.41: Egyptian Free-Tail Bat hanging at mine entrance

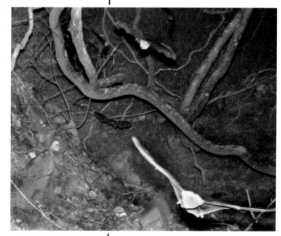

Fig. 2.42: Egyptian Free-Tails emerging from mine

Fig. 2.40: Cape Pangolin

Order Rodentia: Porcupines, Rats, Mice, and Their Allies

Almost half of the mammalian species we have observed at A.U. have been rodents. These mammals play an important role in every African terrestrial ecosystem. Some types have additional economic or cultural significance, and a few varieties have been implicated as significant vectors for or reservoirs of life-threatening diseases (though not explicitly at Africa University).

Fig. 2.43: African Porcupines in a mineshaft later occupied by gold prospectors

Hystrix africaeaustralis, African Porcupine (Fig. 2.43). Not all rodents are small, and the African Porcupine averages about 12kg in mass. The head and shoulders of this unmistakable rodent bear a mane of long, grey-white hair, and the rear two-thirds of the body are protected by a formidable coat of black and white spines. The spines are somewhat flexible, but they are sharp-tipped, and they are long (up to about 50cm), so approaching a porcupine can be a sticky proposition. Furthermore, if harassed sufficiently, a porkey may turn its backend towards you, glance over its shoulder to aim, and charge!

African porcupines spend their days in hiding. At A.U. we have encountered them most frequently in abandoned mineshafts, but they often modify the burrows of other mammals or even dig their own. Porkeys usually shelter in family groups, a female and male, often accompanied by one or more off-spring. At night, however, the animals typically forage alone, and on a late-winter evening you might hear a porkey snuffling through the dried vegetation alongside a back-mountain path.

Porcupines like roots and underground tubers, but they will eat a wide variety of plant material, including many different field crops. They will also gnaw on old mammal bones or even tortoise shells, probably to obtain the calcium and phosphorus that must be mobilized for the production of the porkeys' quills.

When porcupines become agricultural pests, some Zimbabweans will trap them, and we have known American missionaries who proclaim that the flesh tastes like — you guessed it — chicken. On the other hand, *Hystrix africaeaustralis* is the totem-animal for many people in the Mutare area, and these folks are forbidden by custom from even touching the animal.

Any healthy African terrestrial ecosystem will support lots of rats and mice. At A.U. we've live-trapped almost a dozen species, some in more than gratifying abundance.

Aethomys, Veld Rats (Fig. 2.44). Two species of *Aethomys* are common across the campus lowlands. The larger (*A. chrysophilus*) is sometimes called the Red Veld Rat, but although it may be reddish, you should certainly not expect fire-engine coloration. With a mass of about 60-80 grams, this is either a large mouse or a small rat, depending on your feelings about rodent sizes.

Red Veld Rats often live in groups, sheltering in holes that they may dig under rock jumbles or fallen trees. At least in some regions they also mound up piles of grass over the entrances to their burrows.

This rodent probably eats mostly seeds, but during some seasons it supplements that diet with a substantial component of insects. We have often found what we believe to be its hair in the scat of African Pythons.

Fig. 2.44: Red Veld Rat

Fig. 2.45: Two views of the Fat Mouse

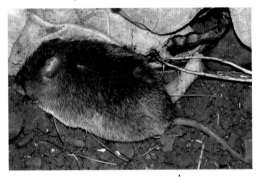

Fig. 2.46: Spiny Mouse

Steatomys pratensis, Fat Mouse (Fig. 2.45). This little rodent certainly deserves its name because it packs almost the weight of a house mouse onto a much shorter body. Fat mice are often found in cultivated areas, where they dig deep, slanting burrows, which they line with shredded leaves and grass.

Reproduction is probably confined mostly to the rainy season, and during winter's cold Fat Mice appear to enter a sort of torpor (to us they look sleepy pretty much all of the time). Like so many other small rodents, Fat Mice eat mostly seeds, but they occasionally take insects and other small invertebrates as well.

Acomys spinosissimus, Spiny Mouse (Fig. 2.46). This is one of our favorite rodents, and Ab has used one of G.R.'s fine pictures as a Christmas card. Spiny mice average perhaps 25-30 grams in mass. They are often associated with rocky terrain, but we have caught them in numerous different campus locations. Sometimes they live communally, but we have also found them alone. Their food consists largely of seeds, but they often add a few termites to the diet.

While teaching at A.U., we have occasionally shown collections of live-trapped mice to our Wildlife Management classes. The reaction toward most species is similar to what one might expect from American students — expressions of boredom, distaste, or even disgust. On the other hand, many Zimbabwean students appreciate spiny mice, observing that when they are boiled, salted, and dried, they can be a delicious treat. We consider these mice too cute to consume on a regular basis, and anyhow we do not know the details of the customary preparation recipe. Nevertheless, we do not wish to denigrate the gastronomic appeal of *A. spinosissimus,* and if offered a salted spiny mouse, we would gladly give the delicacy a try.

Order Carnivora: Meat-eating Mammals

Many of the mice at A.U. eventually fall prey to snakes or birds, but the University campus also supports several species of mammalian predators, and in October of 2000, we twice saw leopard tracks along a road through the northern lowlands. Smaller carnivores, such as mongoose and genet, are much more common.

Genetta genetta, Small-Spotted Genet (Fig. 2.47). This animal may be the most abundant wild carnivore on the A.U. campus. It is a member of the Family Viverridae, which includes other genets as well as civets, palm civets, and a number of other little-known, low-slung, slinky creatures. The Small-Spotted Genet is slightly less than a meter in total length (about half of which is tail), and it has a mass of almost 2kg. It can be found pretty much anywhere in A.U.'s less-developed woodlands, where it seems to prefer the more open patches of ground.

Small-Spotted Genets are strictly nocturnal. For food they exploit mostly mammals and birds, usually targeting creatures weighing less than about 100 grams. The genet's typical approach is cat-like, a stealthy stalk followed by a short rush. Unlike cats, however, genets do not deliver a well-directed killing bite but rather hold onto their prey with sharp claws and bite the unfortunate victim repeatedly, anywhere.

In 2000 we found Small-Spotted Genets to be abundant on the A.U. campus. We still noticed them in 2007, but they seemed to be less common. We would be tempted to attribute any genet decline to the enormous increase on campus of feral domestic cats. We suspect that these cats can out-compete genets in many habitats. Also, they probably take a substantial toll on reptiles and small birds; at any rate, the over-numerous house cats are certainly not an asset to indigenous wildlife at Africa University. On the other hand, given lemons, one should consider the preparation of lemonade. A.U.'s domestic cats could be studied quite easily, and we suggest that this might be an appropriate radio-telemetry project for some ambitious Wildlife Management student.

Order Artiodactyla: Hoofed Mammals

At Africa University we have seen five species of wild hoofed mammals. We shall briefly introduce one of the more common antelopes, and then we shall meditate at some length on bushpigs.

Raphicerus sharpei, Sharpe's Grysbok (Fig. 2.48). This is a small antelope, usually weighing about 7.5kg and standing about 50cm high at the shoulder. These little antelopes are rather poorly known. At A.U. we have observed grysboks only in the densest lowland vegetation, where we believed them to be Red Duikers (another type of small antelope) until we began finding identifiable fragments of teeth and skull (Fig. 2.39).

Grysboks sometimes hide until they are closely approached. Then they may try to sneak away, crouch-walking low to the ground, or they may explode from their thick cover. Probably Sharpe's Grysbok is too small an animal to be an effective ruminant-fermenter of cellulose, so instead of eating grass, this antelope concentrates its diet on tender leaves, occasional seeds, and perhaps a few fruits in season.

Potamochoerus larvatus, Bushpig (Fig. 2.49). We have given this species considerable attention in the Introduction to this book, so we shall now conclude this chapter's mammal section with only a synopsis of the bushpig's natural history. This is a large, rangy animal with lots of hair — and you won't need a field guide to know at a glance that it is most definitely a pig. Males typically weigh about 50-80kg (rarely much more); females are usually a little lighter.

Bushpigs are widely distributed throughout central and east-southern Africa, wherever rainfall is at least moderate and vegetation is dense. The species is particularly widespread in Zimbabwe, sometimes managing to persist even in heavily agricultural areas.

Bushpigs are almost entirely nocturnal and usually move in groups of about three to six, plus, occasionally, a litter of piglets. The dominant boar will defend his group (called a sounder) against other dominant boars and sometimes against potential predators (rarely, even against leopards or people). The size of the home range varies from one habitat to another; males may mark territories by "tusking" trees and bushes around the edges of a feeding ground.

Bushpigs will eat almost any plant material, often digging in soft ground for tubers and roots. Where Vervet Monkeys (*Chlorocebus aethiops*) are common, bushpigs may follow a foraging troop, collecting scraps of fruit that these vigorous primates drop from the trees.

Fig. 2.47: Small-Spotted Genet

Fig. 2.48: Sharpe's Grysbok

Fig. 2.49: Bushpig (sow)

Turtles are the most ancient of all living reptile groups. Indeed, they may be the most ancient of all recognizable reptile groups, living and non-living alike; they appeared way before the dinosaurs and obviously have persisted long after the big-dinosaur demise. We consider turtles a sign that some things abide the ravages of time; we are always glad to see them and proud to tell people about them.

Bushpigs can become serious agricultural pests, raiding maize plots or sugarcane fields. Occasionally they catch and eat small animals, and they have even been known to invade poorly fenced chicken yards, with results more gratifying to the pigs than to the poultry or the farmers.

Baby bushpigs are usually born near the beginning of the rainy season; that way the sow has access to maximum food resources during her energetically costly period of lactation. At parturition a female bushpig may construct a nest of grass, where she will give birth to a litter of about three to four piglets (though litters of up to eight have been reported). The newborns are marked with yellow spots in a striped pattern; this probably serves as camouflage as the piglets hide in the dappled sunshine. Bushpig sows are apparently effective mothers, and juvenile survival is said to be high. The young can mature in as little as 18 months.

In 2000 we commonly observed bushpigs in the lowland forests of Africa University. In 2007 the animals were substantially harder to find.

The Reptiles (Including Birds) of the A.U. Campus

Turtles: Ancient Wonders

The evolutionary origins of turtles are not well understood, and their relationship to other reptiles is currently under debate. Perhaps turtles are descended from some proto-reptile we might call a cotylosaur. (The word is a safe one; it merely means "stem reptile." But it sounds herpetologically sophisticated, so you might wish to use it frequently in casual conversation.) At least in geological terms, the transition from shell-less ancestor to fully formed turtle was rapid: intermediate forms are not known, and in the words of one herpetologist, shelled turtles appear, evolutionarily speaking, "like Athena, springing full-blown from the head of Zeus."

On the Africa University campus we have seen broken shells of an aquatic species known as *Pelomedusa subrufa*. These are flattened, thin-shelled turtles that do not typically occur in crocodile-infested waters, so one might expect to find them in A.U.'s shallow creeks and flooded pans. Nevertheless, although our aquatic-turtle traps caught plenty of fish, crabs, and even frogs, they never presented us with even a single *Pelomedusa*. On the other hand, we have seen several Hingeback Tortoises, a terrestrial species that we shall now consider.

Kinixys belliana, Bell's Hingeback Tortoise (Figs. 2.50-2.52). Although water turtles have eluded our on-campus quests, we have seen several tortoises at Africa University. Our resident species gets its name because its carapace has a hinge (immediately in front of the hind legs; look closely at Fig. 2.51) that allows the animal to pull down the back part of its shell, protecting the softer parts underneath.

Hingies are not large — even females are typically under 20cm long — and most herpetologists believed them to be rather sedentary creatures. For much of the year this assumption is correct. At A.U., from the end of the rainy season until well into the spring, these tortoises usually hunker down amid the rocks on the near mountain. But when the rains return, Hingeback Tortoises emerge to graze on tender new-grass (plus a few leaves and mushrooms). In October of 2000, we attached radio transmitters to two of these attractive little animals. We found that on a good day they can move as much as a kilometer, which certainly seems a prodigious journey for such a small turtle.

The survival of *K. belliana* at A.U. is not something that we are willing to take for granted. These turtles are slow to mature, and they produce only small clutches of eggs (typically 2-7). Some Zimbabweans eat hingies, and if they were hunted with trained dogs, they could be rapidly pushed towards extinction on the University campus.

Fig. 2.51: Hingeback with radio

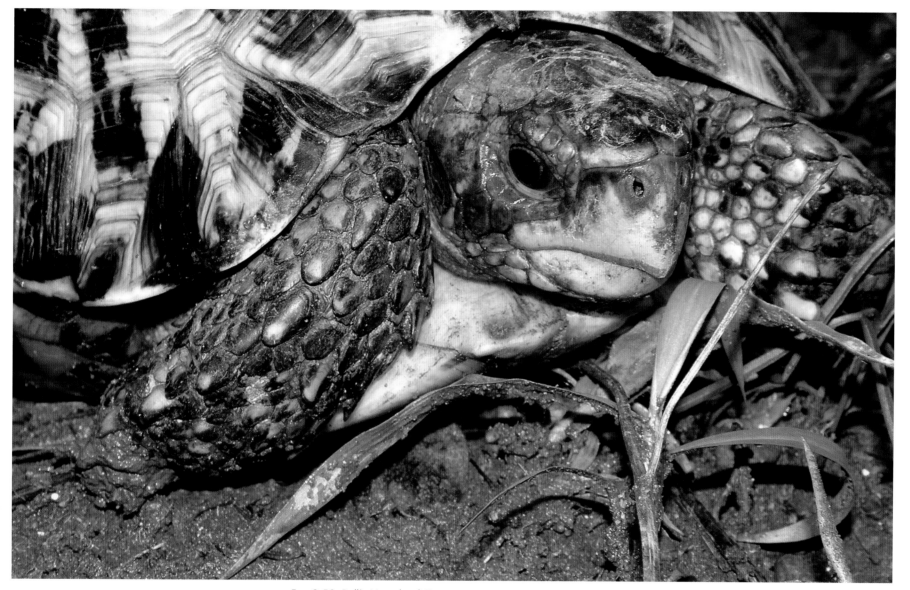

Fig. 2.52: Bell's Hingeback Tortoise

Birds: Diversity above our Heads

Chris and Ab have worked together for years as field herpetologists. We are partial to reptiles, and we never consider the end of the Cretaceous Period without regret over the passing of the biggest, most impressive dinosaurs. Because we are thankful for the archosaurs that did survive into the present, we proudly declare our allegiance to the (correct!) taxonomic position that birds are reptiles, feathered dinosaurs specialized for high-energy thermoregulation and (in most cases) for flight.

In the United States many bird watchers maintain lists of types observed, and for the beginning birder, a list of 100 species is considered to be something of a milestone. At Africa University, if you are diligent, carrying decent binoculars and a field guide everywhere you go, then you can easily surpass this mark in a single semester. (Chris and Ab managed that, and we are definitely not accomplished birders.) We do not know how many bird species have occasionally frequented the A.U. campus. A quick scan of the range maps in Newman's *Birds of Southern Africa* suggests that the number could be between 400 and 500 — which is about like the count for all of South Carolina (a state known for its avian diversity).

During our times at A.U., we did not concentrate any substantial effort on documenting the campus bird life. In part this was because we lack ornithological expertise and because our camera equipment was better suited for

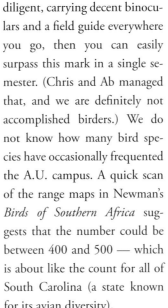

Fig. 2.53: *Uraeginthus angolensis*, Blue Waxbill

Fig. 2.54: Guinea Feathers

frogs in the hand than for birds in the bush. We also have two slightly better excuses for our neglect. First, the bird diversity of southern Africa is exceedingly well-documented: 660 species are known to occur in Zimbabwe, and no in-country ornithologist expects the list to grow appreciably. At least four excellent field guides exist, and in Mutare a birding club has kept extensive records for many years. We simply did not believe that, in our brief visit, we could add to information about the birds of Zimbabwe's Eastern Highlands.

Second, most birds are highly mobile. Because they can fly from place to place — because most species can "island-hop" — unbroken dispersal corridors are relatively unimportant to them. Thus, for birds, the A.U. campus is probably a less critical refuge than it is for amphibians, reptiles, mammals, and some invertebrates.

All these factors not withstanding, we did look at birds when we had opportunity. We were impressed by the number of raptors (hawks, falcons, eagles, etc.), and we were gratified to recognize the songs of several dove species, particularly around sunrise and sunset. As A.U.'s wheat matured, we spent some time with crop guards who protected the fields from invading clouds of Red-Billed Quelea (if you know the

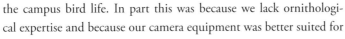

common name, you would recognize the Latin binomial: it's *Qualea qualea*.) We were particularly impressed by the proficiency of one young guard who could shoot her catapult (slingshot) like a rifle. One species of weaver nested in our front yard, and several other kinds hung their pendulous nests over the waters where we looked for frogs and snakes. We watched flocks of Helmeted Guinea Fowl patrol the ecotone between field and forest; on our way to class, we listened to their raucous calls every morning. On our night walks we often saw Red-Necked Francolin; we released one from a poacher's snare — and felt guilty for depriving somebody of a decent meal.

All in all, we are sorry that we did not get to know our avian neighbors a bit better. We intend them no slight, and by way of apology we'll show you several bird pictures — and then move on to some more earthbound reptiles.

Fig. 2.55: Left to right, these birds are Melba Finch (*Pytilia melba*), Abdim's Stork (*Ciconia abdimii*) and Spotted Eagle Owl (*Bubo africanus*)

Fig. 2.56: *Mabuya striata*, Striped Skink

Squamates (Lizards and Snakes)

Every natural historian knows that, in terms of raw abundance or of species diversity, vertebrates are little more than a sideshow in the Circus of Life. Bacteria are the reigning Kingdom, with uncounted species in almost every habitat and with individuals whose numbers approach those of the stars.

Considering only animals that you can see without a microscope, insects are the unquestionable champions. In numbers of species, beetles by themselves exceed the entire Vertebrata by perhaps a factor of 10. Still, amongst the vertebrates, in terms of species diversity, four especially successful taxa can be recognized.

These are the ray-finned fish, the frogs, the perching birds, and the squamate reptiles. Elsewhere in this book we have praised the wonder of frogs, and we have offered a paragraph explaining why the fish are not particularly diverse in southern Africa. Unfortunately, we have not done the University birds any real justice, so if you manage to visit our campus, you should bring a telephoto lens and add some photos of feathered friends to our bestiary. Anyhow, having discussed the frogs (and dispensed with fish and birds) we are now left with lizards and snakes as representatives of the truly successful vertebrates. And we joyfully turn to their consideration.

According to the best field guides for southern African reptiles, the squamate fauna of Zimbabwe's Manicaland region is impressive at any taxonomic level, with about twice as many Families, twice as many genera, and twice as many species as our entire home state of South Carolina. Furthermore, since the variety of A.U. landscapes is so great — we have hills, valleys, ponds, streams, rocks, fields, and forests — many of these species should be found on campus. For some squamates, this diversity is easy to document. Many lizard-species are readily visible to even the casual observer. Skinks sun themselves on and around the academic buildings, small geckos share most of the staff houses, plated lizards can be observed near the front gate, and any visitor who stays into the rainy season should eventually see a chameleon stalking its slow way across a campus road.

On the other hand, snakes in general are secretive, and southern Africa possesses a wealth of burrowing lizards that are poorly known even to professional herpetologists. Anyhow, including both the obvious and the elusive, a list of on-campus squamates might approach 100 species; to date we have managed to photograph only about 20% of them.

We shall proceed immediately to a consideration of four representative lizard Families, beginning with the Scincidae. After that we'll signal our transition into the snakes by providing some general information about that fascinating group.

Fig. 2.57: *Dasypeltis scabra*, Rhombic Egg-Eating Snake

Lizards, Family Scincidae

This, the largest Family of lizards, includes about 100 genera and approximately 1100 species. Skinks range throughout most of the tropical and temperate world, even including many isolated Pacific islands. The body form is variable, but the majority of skinks look a good bit alike. The skin is typically shiny; the head is not usually distinct from the neck; the body is small and brown; the legs are short. Skink scales, which appear almost polished, overlap. Also, the scales are reinforced by underlying plates of dermal bone, and snakes with short, sharp teeth have difficulty holding onto these lizards. Although many skinks are diurnal, most are also secretive, foraging in leaf litter or under bark, so they are not often seen except when they are basking.

Mabuya striata, Striped Skink (Figs. 2.56 and 2.58). This is a large skink, typically about 75mm snout-vent length. Its robust build, distinct dark eye-line, and crisp white dorso-lateral stripes should distinguish it from the somewhat similar Variable Skink. Beginning in early spring, Striped Skinks are frequently seen around human dwellings, basking in the morning sun and then foraging on house sides, rock outcrops, or trees. In our experience, this is the lizard most commonly observed on the A.U. campus.

Fig. 2.58: Striped Skink

Proscelotes arnoldi, Arnold's Skink (Fig. 2.59). This is a slender, small lizard (about 60mm snout-vent length) with a long tail. The back is brown and shiny, often with a hint of dark, dorso-lateral stripes. The belly is pinkish, and the underside of the tail appears almost red. At Africa University we have found the species exclusively in the campus lowlands, usually under rotting logs. Even within the species' small range (a strip of land spanning the central border between Zimbabwe and Mozambique), reproduction is variable: some females lay eggs, and some bear their young alive.

Fig. 2.59: Arnold's Skink

Family Gerrhosauridae

The Gerrhosauridae, with six genera and about 30 species, occurs not only on the African continent but also on Madagascar, and its evolution is thought to pre-date the separation of this island from the African mainland. Gerrhosaurids have rectangular, plate-like scales arranged in regular rows circling the body, and a lateral skin-fold runs from neck to tail. Gerrhosaurids make acceptable pets and have been known to live in captivity for over 15 years.

Gerrhosaurus flavigularis, Yellow-Throated Plated Lizard (Figs. 2.60-2.61). This is a big animal (about 120mm snout-vent) with a rounded body and proportionally small head. At Africa University the dorsal coloration is a rich reddish-brown. A yellowish-white dorso-lateral stripe, narrowly bordered by black, extends from the head to almost the tip of the tail. During the spring breeding season, the chin, throat, and anterior flanks of the male turn deep red. The female buries a clutch of about 6 eggs, often in a cavity under a flat rock.

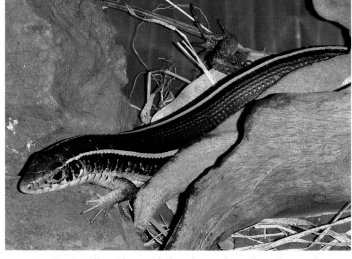

Fig. 2.60: Yellow-Throated Plated Lizard, non-breeding male

Fig. 2.61: Yellow-Throated Plated Lizard, breeding male (note red color)

We have seen this active, terrestrial forager in several areas of the campus, but in our experience it can be most readily observed near the entrance gate, patrolling the rocky outcrop where the national and university flags are raised.

Fig. 2.62: Flap-Necked Chameleon (wearing gray-brown)

Fig. 2.63: Flap-Necked Chameleon (wearing yellow)

Family Chamaeleonidae

The Family includes 4-6 genera and about 130 species (most of which are in the nominate genus, *Chamaeleo*). The range of the Chamaeleonidae is non-Saharan Africa, extreme south Spain, coastal Arabia, Madagascar, India, and Sri Lanka. At least one chameleon species has been widely introduced in suburban Hawaii. This most distinct Family of lizards includes highly specialized, generally arboreal insectivores. They are best known for their ability to change colors, but chameleons also have other unique adaptations, such as grasping feet and tails, vertically flattened bodies, long tongues, and turret-shaped eyes.

Chamaeleo dilepis, Flap-Necked Chameleon (Figs. 2.62-2.64). Whatever color these lizards may turn — and they can be pretty much any shade of green or yellow as well as gray or grayish-brown — chameleons are unmistakable.

The snout-vent length is typically about 125mm; the body is vertically flattened. The eyes function in apparent independence. The tail is prehensile, and the feet are zygodactylus (with digits arranged in two opposable sets, like parrots' feet). The animal hunts for small arthropods, especially beetles and grasshoppers, stalking them in bushes and small trees. Even in hot pursuit, a chameleon moves very slowly, sometimes gliding along a branch, sometimes rocking back and forth as if trying to estimate the range to its insect-prey. (This is done by evaluating focus and not, as previously assumed, by triangulation.) When a chameleon gets sufficiently close to its target, the insect is captured by a flick of the sticky tongue.

Reproductive activities are vigorous, with males engaging in active combat. Females lay very large clutches (reportedly, about 25-65) of small eggs in shallow holes in moist soil. Perhaps because of this high reproductive investment, by both genders, chameleons are usually short-lived.

These lizards are entirely harmless to people, but when harassed a chameleon will inflate its body, gape its mouth, and hiss softly. It will also bite readily, and perhaps for this reason (plus its general strange-

Fig. 2.64: Flap-Necked Chameleon (wearing green)

ness) the species is feared by a few local folks. Legends about chameleons abound. The one we've heard most frequently goes something like this:

> *Perhaps you have noticed that chameleons move very slowly. Well, this is related to one of God's few mistakes. At the beginning of time, when evil entered the world, God wanted to warn his people that Death was coming, and God chose an animal messenger to carry the bad news. Unfortunately, this messenger happened to be the chameleon. When you see one of these lizards moving slowly across your path today, it is saying to itself, "I must hurry; I must hurry; I must warn people that Death is coming."*

At Africa University chameleons are not terrifically common, but we have seen them near the dorms, on the near mountain, in the undeveloped lowlands, and along the road leading to the old tilapia ponds. Because of their cryptic coloration, chameleons are difficult to find, and they are best hunted at night, when they show up as white-green against a darker background of leaves. These lizards are highly photogenic, and a chameleon photograph by Terry Ferguson hangs in Wofford's Biology Department suite.

Family Gekkonidae

This large Family contains about 100 genera and approximately 1000 species. Range is basically circumtropical. Geckos are typically small. Their skin is tender and in many species does not appear scaly to the naked eye. Unlike most other lizards, geckos are primarily nocturnal. (There are also a few daytime-active species — many bright green — typically living on isolated islands free of diurnal lizard competitors.) The eyes of many species are unusual for at least two reasons: they often have weirdly shaped pupils, and they usually lack movable eyelids. Many species of geckos also have highly adapted feet (Fig. 2.65). Toe pads, composed of thousands of spatulate microscales, allow these lizards to cling to vertical and even inverted surfaces. By and large, geckos are sit-and-wait predators (or, at most, short-dash hunters).

Pachydactylus punctatus, Speckled Thick-Toed Gecko. This little gecko (median snout-vent length about 30mm) is heavy-bodied with granular skin and a very fat tail. Coloration is said to be varied, but A.U. specimens are usually brick-red with tiny speckles that may be darker brown or yellow-gold.

Speckled Thick-Toed Geckos inhabit burrows in sandy soil, always under some object such as a rock or log. Unseen by day, they emerge at night to forage for small arthropods. Eggs are laid in pairs, supposedly in mid-summer. We have not found *P. punctatus* to be common on our campus, but we have observed them (always by turning rocks) on both sides of the near mountain.

When harassed, if this gentle gecko cannot easily slip away, it will lower its head against the ground and hold its tail high (Fig. 2.66). This posture is said to imitate scorpions and perhaps thereby deter predators that might fear a painful sting.

Fig. 2.65: *Hemidactylus mabouia*,
House Gecko,
underside and close-up of foot

Fig. 2.66: Speckled Thick-Toed Gecko

Hidden Mysteries:
A Few On-Campus Snake Species

The higher classification of snakes has been in a state of flux for many years and will probably stay that way for some time to come. This abiding uncertainty has two fundamental causes. (1) Some snake-species look alike because they are closely related while other snake-species look alike because they have evolved similar adaptations. (2) Snake bones are often small and fragile, so the group's fossil record is not sufficiently complete to sort out every question of relationship. These two conceptually simple problems lie at the heart of 21st century classification biology and therefore merit a bit more discussion.

Modern taxonomy classifies species according to closeness of relationship. Technically, species A & B are said to be more closely related to each other than to Species C if A & B share a more recent common ancestor than either does with Species C. Given an imperfect fossil record, shared ancestry is difficult to demonstrate, so decisions about ancestry and relationship are based largely on how "similar" a set of living species are. Of course similarity of appearance certainly can signify closeness of relationship. On the other hand when two

or more species, only distantly related, exploit separate but similar econiches in similar ways, their evolutionary adaptations are likely to be similar. And these evolutionary adaptations will result in unrelated end-products that are, well, similar. This phenomenon, called convergence, has for more than a century challenged taxonomists trying to decide who-all are similar because they are actually related *versus* who-all are similar only because they have been similarly tailored to similar environments by evolution.

Convergence is particularly problematic for snake taxonomists because the fundamental, underlying ophidian body plan does not lend itself to radically varying expressions. Over the course of about 100 million years, snakes have been "fine-tuned" into many different genera and species, but all these genera and species are very obvious in their basic "snakiness": that is, ecological false-cognates are common because there are only a limited number of ways to be "snakey." Thus, for example, an arid-land ambush snake in southern Africa will of necessity be built somewhat like an arid-land ambush snake in central Australia or in western Arizona, even if these snake species are the end products of very different evolutionary lineages. In other words, the descendents of unrelated snake-ancestors sometimes evolved to look

snakes

Fig. 2.68: *Causus defilippii*, Snouted Night-Adder

Modern herpetologists are generally agreed that snakes are a diverse group of squamates whose evolutionary trajectory began as a highly derived branch of the enormously successful lizard evolutionary tree. We estimate that the world is blessed with 2500-3000 species of snakes. Of these, about 40 species probably occur on the Africa University campus.

Fig. 2.67: *Lamprophis capensis*, Brown House Snake

a lot alike, and this confused early taxonomists, who were deciding "closeness of relationship" by evaluating "similarity of living species."

In practical classification work, the sorting of snake species and even of genera is not terribly difficult, especially given modern techniques of molecular taxonomy. However, as we said, higher classification — the evolutionary choreography of more ancient divergences — is masked by convergence and the obscurity of the ophidian fossil record. And we are far from certain about the detailed organization of the 10-15 Families of living snakes.

In Wofford's herpetology course, Ab tries to bypass the confusion. He flat-out decrees that all snakes can be clustered into four evolutionarily meaningful groups. These we can call the Small-Mouthed Burrowers, the Transitional Snakes, the Early Advanced Snakes, and the Most Recent Advanced Snakes. Except for the Transitional Snakes, all of these groups are represented on the A.U. campus. Our survey of representative species at A.U. begins with the Small-Mouthed Burrowers. Departing from taxonomic order, we next consider the Most Recent Advanced Snakes. That's because we want to discuss Early Advanced Snakes (the giant snakes, boas, pythons, and their allies) last — and thereby conclude this chapter by telling about a very special python.

Fig. 2.69: Delalande's Beaked Blind Snake

Small-Mouthed Burrowers: Family Typhlopidae and Allies

The Small-Mouthed Burrowers are sometimes called "Blind Snakes" (though they are not entirely blind) or "Worm Snakes," (though this name is shared by several species of small, Most Recent Advanced Snakes). Technically, the SMBs are known as the Scolecophidia. The group includes three Families that are distinguished by dental characteristics — whether they have teeth in the upper jaw only, teeth in the lower jaw only, or teeth in both jaws. Two of these Families are found on the A.U. campus. Worldwide, Small-Mouthed Burrowers are mostly circumtropical in distribution. Whereas Advanced and Transitional Snakes have small dorsal scales and wide belly-scales, the SMBs have small scales of about the same size all the way around their bodies.

Typically, scolecophidians are small (10cm-80cm), cylindrical, poor-vision, burrowing animals with strongly reinforced skulls. These rigid skulls, so useful in burrowing, constrain the dimensions of the snakes' gape; therefore, unlike snakes in general, scolecophidians are restricted to prey that is skinny, small, or easily breakable. A few Small-Mouthed Burrowers are worm-eaters, but most specialize on the larvae of ants and (especially) termites. They are probably somewhat like the world's first snakes, but since they are highly successful and display numerous evolutionary specializations for their way of life, they should probably not be called "primitive."

The scolecophidian Family Typhlopidae includes about 165 species, ranging through the West Indies, southern Central America, South America, sub-Saharan Africa, west, south, and Southeast Asia, Papua-Australia, and some Pacific islands. The largest typhlopids can approach a meter in length, but some smaller species are no bigger than the lead in a wooden pencil. Although the eyes are covered with scales, you can see them if you look carefully. So, although they are often called "blind snakes," typhlopids are probably not entirely blind. Teeth are in the upper jaw only. Very little is known about the life histories of these snakes. One of the smallest species, *Ramphotyphlops braminus*, is sometimes called the Flowerpot Snake because it has hitchhiked around the tropics in the soil of ornamental plants. Presently it is the only species of snake established in Hawaii.

Rhinotyphlops lalandei, Delalande's Beaked Blind Snake (Fig. 2.69). This is a moderately slender species with a maximum snout-vent length of about 350mm. As the common and Latin names suggest, the head of *R. lalandei* is horizontally wedged-shaped, with a broad rostral scale used to scrape tunnels through the soil.

Usually this animal's dorsal coloration is slate-gray, but when viewed with a hand lens, scales on the back are seen to be edged in white. The belly may be gray or pink. Because their prey — mostly termite larvae — live underground, these snakes are seldom seen except when forced to the surface by heavy rains.

Rhinotyphlops schlegelii, Schlegel's Beaked Blind Snake. This is the largest of the Small-Mouthed Burrowers, with some specimens approaching a meter in snout-vent length.

Because *R. schlegelii* spends almost all its life underground, evolutionary selection for cryptic coloration has been minimal, and several distinctly noncamouflaged patterns exist. A few individuals are striped, others are dark brownish-gray, and others are white with black blotches (Fig. 2.70). Females are reported to lay large clutches of eggs that hatch in about a month and a half. Sub-adult specimens are frequently driven out of hiding by summer rains, but the larger animals almost never leave their underground world.

Most Recent Advanced Snakes:
Superfamily Colubroidea

This widely distributed group includes about 90% of all living snake species. It also includes all venomous species, and all snake species occurring in our home state of South Carolina. The earliest fossils definitely attributable to this group date from the Oligocene Period (about 30 million years ago). Critical events in the group's paleo-history took place in Southeast Asia, from which many taxa eventually spread. The colonization of Africa was complex and probably occurred in several phases.

The taxonomic organization of the Most Recent Advanced Snakes has been controversial for more than 100 years. Some herpetologists would name as few as three Families; others would list as many as

15. Field guides suggest that the A.U. campus should have about 35 species of these modern snakes, which we divide into five Families, of which we shall illustrate the composite Family "Colubridae," the Family Causidae, and the Family Elapidae.

The two African Families that we shall not discuss are the Atractaspididae and the Viperidae. The former group includes a few venomous species (the burrowing asps) with long, folding fangs as well as some rather obscure harmless animals. In 1993 we saw a roadkilled Bibron's Burrowing Asp on campus. The true vipers (Viperidae) all deliver venom by means of folding fangs in the front of the mouth. In Africa, most are nocturnal, most are heavy-bodied ambush predators, and most are dangerous. In thousands of hours of on-campus field work, we have not discovered even one "true viper," so we do not illustrate them in this book. On the other hand, visitors should be aware that Puff Adders have frequently been observed on roads near Old Mutare.

The Composite "Family Colubridae"

Worldwide, this group includes about 1600 species (over half of all living snakes). Most are entirely harmless, but two on-campus species are rear-fanged and dangerously venomous. These latter creatures are the boomslang (seen occasionally in A.U.'s trees; males are green and females are gray-brown) and the twig snake (which we have not observed on campus, but which should be here; it's a skinny treesnake with an elongated head). Neither of these colubrid species should pose any danger to anybody who leaves them alone.

Over the years we have seen seven "colubrid" species on the A.U. campus. And, below, we shall consider a representative member of this enormous "Family."

Dasypeltis scabra, Rhombic Egg-Eating Snake (Figs. 2.57 and 2.71). These slender little snakes have many adaptations for eating bird eggs. The skin of the neck and the connection between the lower jaws can stretch enormously. Their mouths have only the tiniest teeth, but two vertebral projections extend into the throat and chip/saw their way through an egg that is being swallowed. The col-

Fig. 2.70: Schlegel's Beaked Blind Snake

2.71: Rhombic Egg-Eating Snake

lapsed shell is then regurgitated while the nutritious liquid is swallowed. Though common, Egg Eaters are seldom seen because they are nocturnal and because they must concentrate their foraging activities during the limited season when birds are nesting. Some wild-caught specimens will adjust readily if you can provide them with a generous supply of small eggs, and one Egg Eater lived in captivity for over 30 years.

Family Causidae

These snakes, commonly called night adders, are typically short and stout. They are venomous, they have moderately long erectile fangs, and if sufficiently pestered, they will bite. Usually, however, they are inoffensive, and even if a bite should occur, it is unlikely to be medically significant.

Causus defilippii, Snouted Night-Adder. This chubby little snake is said to be abundant in the Mutare area, but we have seen only one specimen in all our time at Africa University (Fig. 2.72; see also Fig. 2.68). Probably Snouted Night-Adders feed almost entirely on frogs and toads, and probably they fall victim frequently to ophiophagous snakes such as the Snouted Cobra (Fig. 2.73).

Family Elapidae

The Family is characterized by non-folding fangs in the front of the mouth. Many species are dangerous, and all are venomous to some degree. The typical elapid venom has neurotoxic effects, often impeding the ability of a victim to breathe.

Worldwide this group has almost 300 species in about 62 genera. The present range of the elapids is southeastern and southwestern United States, Mexico, Central America, tropical South America, Africa (except the driest deserts), South and Southeast Asia, and Australia. Furthermore, if you include the sea snakes in this Family — and you probably should — then the Elapidae may also be said to inhabit much of the Indian and Pacific Oceans. In Australia elapids are particularly diverse and occupy many econiches held by other snake Families on other continents.

On the A.U. campus we once saw, at a distance, what we took to be a Mozambican Spitting Cobra (*Naja mossambica*), and in 2007 we saw a big Black Mamba (*Dendroaspis polylepis*) at closer range than we might have wished. We have encountered Snouted Cobras (*Naja annulifera*) much more frequently.

Naja annulifera, Snouted Cobra. Until recently, many herpetologists lumped this southern animal into the same species as the big, generalized cobra of more northern Africa. (This latter animal, *Naja haje*, is usually called the Egyptian Cobra.) Snouted Cobras are now considered a separate species because their nostrils are displaced farther behind the nose tip and are oriented slightly rearward. Perhaps this makes it easier for old *N. annulifera* to breathe while it pokes around in holes and leaf litter, seeking toads and snakes.

N. annulifera is a big snake, with some males exceeding 2m snout-vent length. Older animals are often uniformly dark in color; younger specimens may be brownish-yellow. Some individuals have broad bands of alternating black and yellow, hence the Latin speciesname. The Snouted Cobra is an active forager, usually hunting small vertebrates at dusk or in the nighttime. Favorite food items include lizards, toads, rodents, and other snakes; perhaps, in fact, the apparent absence of puff adders from the A.U. campus is attributable to the abundance of this cobra.

Unlike most Zimbabweans, we are quite fond of Snouted Cobras (though we might fear them much more if we had children living within their habitat). We have never found the species to be even

Fig. 2.72: Snouted Night-Adder

Fig. 2.73: Snouted Cobra

Early Advanced Snakes: Family Boidae and Allies

In his herp course at Wofford College, Ab neglects some recent molecular taxonomy and includes three Families in the Early Advanced Snakes. The two Families we shan't discuss are the Bolyeridae (two highly endangered species of small snake that inhabit Round Island in the Indian Ocean) and the Tropidophiidae (20 species of small, New World snakes whose distribution is centered in the West Indies). The third Family, the Boidae, includes the boas and anacondas as well as the pythons, which were formerly placed in their own separate Family.

Boid snakes were probably distributed worldwide by the end of dinosaur-times, and they now range throughout almost all of the humid tropics. Most boids are big; indeed, the Family includes the largest living snakes. All boids are constrictors, and all are capable of eating prey that is large proportional to their body size.

Snakes in general are adapted to exploit relatively large prey, and because snakes must swallow their food whole, this big-food strategy presents a serious biomechanical challenge. Anatomically, the issue is, "How do you get large-diameter foodstuff into a small-diameter tube, when that tube has no equipment for slicing the foodstuff into pieces of convenient size?" In a herpetology class, students learn that the tube can stretch a whole lot, and that the mouth of the tube can stretch a whole, whole lot. Specific swallowing-adaptations include a flexible braincase, near independence of the lower jaws, and elongation of articulating bones that define the mouth-perimeter. So, almost all advanced snakes are good at feats of prodigious swallowing — but big boids (like pythons) are the real champions!

Typically, predators specializing in large prey must be able to move substantial distances. And the success of Early Advanced Snakes was accompanied by the evolution of broad belly-scales, which facilitate long-distance crawling. Of course large-prey specialists must also have some efficient means of killing their food, and boids do this by constriction.

Many boids have attractive skin-patterns, some of which have been used commercially for boots, handbags, and other fashion accesso-

"Biology can now tell stories about butterflies, zebras, and leopards that I contend are every bit as enchanting as Kipling's fairy tales."

Sean Carroll

slightly aggressive, and the individual we photographed for this book could scarcely be induced to spread its hood. Nevertheless, if you harass a Snouted Cobra sufficiently, it will eventually turn, spread its hood, and confront you with considerable spunk. Individuals from southwestern Africa are said to be more irascible, but we cannot vouch for this claim.

In 2000, a large female Snouted Cobra lived in the savanna-lawn that fronts A.U.'s Ireson-Kurewa Building, and she was often seen basking on a termite mound. Taking advantage of her highly visible presence, two male students from Malawi hired themselves out as "snake guides," who would escort more fearful students past the cobra's lair. (They gave reduced rates to pretty coeds.) These enterprising young men were not happy when we caught the cobra and evicted her to a safer part of campus (Fig. 2.18, much earlier in the chapter). In 2007 a very large Snouted Cobra, of the banded phase, repeatedly attempted to raid the A.U. Farm's layer house. We hunted for this animal again and again, and on several nights we waited for hours in or around the layer house. But we never saw the big cobra.

ries. Boas and pythons have also been exploited for the exotic-pet market (though today most pet boas and pythons are captive-bred). Because of such threats, the Family as a whole now receives limited protection under the Convention on International Trade of Endangered Species.

Pythons are animals of the Eastern Hemisphere, and all species lay eggs. The distribution of boas is more complex, and almost all bear their young alive. The only boid snake at A.U. is the Southern Rock Python, *Python natalensis*. The Latin name for this species (recently separated from the more northerly *P. sebae*) is taken from the South African province currently known as Kwa-Zulu Natal. Natal (literally, "birth") is the Portuguese word for Christmas. So, sometimes we like to call our A.U. boid "the Christmas Python."

Fig. 2.74: Southern Rock Python

Family Boidae

Python natalensis, Southern Rock Python (Figs. 2.74-2.76). The Rock Python is a long (potentially very long), solidly-built snake with a broad, triangular head and a dorsal coloration of dark blotches against a background of olive, tan, or silver-gray. This excellent animal — legally, a protected species throughout Zimbabwe — is well-known on the Africa University campus. And, as you will see, it has become an important snake in our lives.

Back in 1898, when Bishop Joseph Hartzell received his land-grant for Old Umtali, he could readily appreciate the scenic beauty and agricultural potential of the area. Still, the American churchman might not have initially realized the full extent of his good fortune. He might not have known that his lands were — and would remain — blessed with an abundance of pythons.

In order to live long and prosper, African pythons must have three things: water, shelter, and an abundance of food. These requirements, of course, apply to wildlife in general, but *Python natalensis* needs such resources scaled for a hatchling that could fit into your pocket and for an adult that could weigh more than you do. Around Africa University, creeks, pans, and irrigation canals can supply water throughout most of the year, and the Mutare River never runs completely dry. Crevasses, caves, and abandoned mineshafts can serve as hideaways, but termiteria (whose entrances vary more in size than do the diameters of pythons) are most commonly used for shelter. The mounds of some termite species are icebergian in extent: their visible proportions scarcely hint at what is hidden below the surface. In this underground world, channels and chambers — any of which may be enlarged by sundry vertebrate inhabitants — offer refuges whose temperature and humidity remain constantly within python-acceptable limits. And when the clay surface of a mound bakes hard into laterite, these refuges become almost impregnable.

Food for *P. natalensis* is also abundantly available on the A.U. campus. A hungry Rock Python will sometimes forage actively, but more often it will crawl cross-country, investigating the substrate with flicks of its forked tongue. Then, when it detects the smell of a well-used animal trail, the python will hide in ambush, ready to aim a

strike by sight, by smell, or by infrared images that its heat-sensitive labial pits can "see." Perhaps because these lip organs can detect an animal's heat signature against a cooler background, *P. natalensis* eats almost exclusively warm-blooded vertebrates. On our campus, mice abound in both density and species variety, so during their hatchling year, A.U.'s pythons probably subsist largely on these small rodents. Maturing youngsters convert to rats, plus some rabbits and a few birds. Over the years we have examined the scat left by adult pythons: identifiable remains have included rodent hair, a few claws from small mammalian carnivores, and many horns and hoofs from campus antelopes.

The maturation rate of wild *P. natalensis* is not known. In captivity, kept warm and fed all it will eat, a healthy specimen can exceed 2.5m in length within the hatchling year. In the wild this does not happen: young pythons grow little during Zimbabwe's chilly winters, and, even in summer, depredation from ambush is largely a matter of luck: some days you get the Veld Rat; most days you do not. Fortunately, African pythons are well-adapted for the feast-or-famine existence of an ambush predator. They are capable of very long fasts (for big adults, fasts can exceed a year in the most extreme cases), lowering their metabolic rate to bare-existence levels. Then, when prey comes along, a python will take it — and, within immodest limits, the bigger the better. In other words, pythons hardly ever starve, so, although maturation can be quite slow, some pythons hang on, avoid the hazards of life for a few years, and eventually reach sexual maturity.

When the days grow shorter and the nights become cooler, Rock Pythons feed less frequently, and adults are likely to begin reproductive behavior. As with most other snakes, these activities are mediated largely through smell. Special glands around the cloaca (the anal vent) produce pheromones with odors recognizable by other snakes of the same species. When a patrolling male Rock Python detects the special scent from the cloacal glands of a female, he will follow her trail, perhaps for many hours, perhaps confronting and briefly fighting another male along the way.

After he finds the female, she will not be receptive to mating until she has been properly courted. The male may begin by rubbing his chin along the back of the female while moving his head from side to side in short, stuttering jerks. Eventually the female will align her body beside his, and he will begin to caress her with his cloacal spurs (which are, anatomically, very short vestigial legs). After this behavior has continued for some time, the female will finally lift her tail and allow the male to mate.

Within about three months after mating, the female will lay a whole bunch of eggs (50-100 for a really big, well-fed momma) — and they're almost as big as tennis balls. Most snakes abandon their eggs (or live-born young) immediately, but pythons are different. The female seeks a secluded spot (a termite mound, a mineshaft, whatever), lays her eggs, and coils around them. In other large python species, a brooding female will generate heat by initiating a series of contractions reminiscent of shivering in mammals. But in *P. natalensis* a mother python will bask occasionally, capturing the midday heat of Zimbabwe's winter sun; then she will crawl back to her lair to warm her eggs. In any case, the clutch will be maintained at about 30°C for the protracted incubation period (2-3 months). Typically eggs hatch at the beginning of the summer rains, when food and thermal resources for the young are most readily available. At that point the mother (apparently) loses all interest. And that is understandable; after all, she has endured a whole lot of very hard work throughout a very long fast, and she needs to go about the business of rebuilding her own resources (small antelope beware!).

"Consider the lilies of the field, how they grow; they neither toil nor spin, yet I tell you, even Solomon in all his glory was not clothed like one of these."

Matthew 6:28-29

A.U. Pythons:
Up Close and Personal

We have some familiarity with *P. natalensis* on the Africa University campus. In 2007 we caught two pythons. The first was a 2m youngster found in a mole rat colony. As you can see from Fig. 2.75, this python was not at the peak of the species' beauty. The cloudy eyes indicate that the animal would soon shed its skin, and the engorged ticks suggest that this snake had been spending a substantial amount of time in mammal burrows.

The second 2007 python was a freshly shed subadult that we discovered one spring night about 50m behind our house. Although African pythons can be quite snappy, this animal was very calm; we kept it for several days, and it posed readily for photographs (Fig. 2.76).

Back in 2000 we had found a slightly smaller python, and we implanted a radio transmitter into the animal's pleuroperitoneal cavity. This enabled us to instruct our Wildlife students in the finer points of radio telemetry, and we were able to keep up with the whereabouts of the snake for almost 100 days.

Although our radio-python spent a considerable amount of time underground, in termite nests, it was also a real mover, sometimes covering over a kilometer in a single day. We were interested to note that the python used every major on-campus habitat-type (and it once ventured off campus, by about 10 meters), sometimes ambushing in a flooded lowland field, sometimes hunting in the mountain rocks. Movement between these areas required that the snake traverse a broad agricultural landscape; inevitably it made these crossings by crawling along a narrow, overgrown fence line. This landscape feature, which in 2000 we called "the Python Corridor," was also used by several other vertebrate species. It had been cleared by 2007. In Fig. 2.77, we outline the "corridor" in red.

When I (Ab Abercrombie) talked proudly about our radio-python, folks from Old Mutare would always ask about its size, and they would disparage the entire telemetry enterprise when they learned that our animal was only a little longer than the height of a tall man. "Wait until you see the big one," they would say; "it's six meters long — a real python." I was somewhat sensitive about the dimensions of my favorite python. Besides, I'd read the books, and I understood that

Fig. 2.75: Southern Rock Python, pre-shedding, with ticks

no python of near-record size could possibly survive in the agricultural heartland of modern Zimbabwe. So, with a generous ration of academic scorn, I would refute my disparagers. "There is no six-meter python around here! I know things like that; I have a Ph.D."

Then, in December of 2000, at the advent of the summer rains, I had trekked to the southeastern edge of campus to examine a mineshaft where I had previously photographed a pair of porcupines. The porkeys were not at home, and it was with some disap-

Fig. 2.76: Southern Rock Python

pointment that I descended the mountain slope to ford the Mutare River (there being no log-bridge at the time). I had entered a dense thicket in the narrow flood plain of the Mutare and was forcing my way through the *Phragmites* stems, which were almost twice my height, when my eye caught a flash of sunlight on silver-gray scales. And there it was, stretched full-length by the riverside, the Python of pythons. There is no way I can describe this enormous snake; that would be like explaining what love is or like describing the Seraphim. For any person of the modern world, words would degenerate into silliness: "Each one had six wings; with twain he covered his face, and with twain he covered his feet, and with twain he did fly." As a scientist, I wish I could have laid a tape measure along the snake; as a wildlifer, I wish I could have implanted a transmitter. And by gosh I'd have done those things if I possibly could have. But this was not a snake measurable in centimeters or locatable by radio pulses. It was a snake outside of size and place; it was a snake belonging to the deep nature of life itself.... Heck, I told you that words degenerate into silliness. Here is the simple truth. That snake was the best single thing that has ever happened to me, and I shall never want anything better. This was the real *Python natalensis*, the Christmas Python. (And someday, maybe, I'll tell people how big I really think it was.)

On 12 February of 2009, the 200th anniversary of Charles Darwin's birth, I found myself working on this book. I thought about the many times I had discussed with my students the towering intellectual achievements of modern evolutionary theory. "The only way to learn how the world has become filled with so many fascinating organisms," I say, "is to study evolution." I believe that 100%, and I certainly would never turn to the book of Genesis for biology lessons. But once in a great while something so devastating or so sad or so wonderful happens to you that explanations of "how" just don't seem quite sufficient. Then, perhaps, when in tears and exultation you confront the existential question of "why," then perhaps you might turn to the Story of Creation. And when you see a wild python as magnificent as the one I saw, then you will surely sing, with Mr. Watts, "He formed the creatures at his word, And then pronounced them good."

Chris and Ab believe that a world without enormous pythons — or tiny geckos or medium-sized guinea fowl — would be a world immeasurably poorer than the one we enjoy. And we believe that an A.U. campus without these creatures would be out of harmony with the stewardship teachings of the United Methodist Church. We have discussed these beliefs with G.R. and Terry and a host of other colleagues. We have no great collective wisdom about how to conserve the priceless flora and fauna of Africa University's land, just as we do not know with certainty how to keep alive the human hopes and dreams described in the two other chapters of this book. But we will not turn away from these issues, and in a separate section after G.R.'s "Farm" chapter, we shall list some simple suggestions — in the hope that you will improve upon them.

Fig. 2.77: "Python Corridor"

Chapter 2 Appendix

If you go to visit A.U., you'll have the most fun if you limit the personal stuff in your baggage and mostly take items that you can give away. On the other hand, if you do want to explore the campus for critters, you should probably have decent footwear, a hat, a raincoat (in season), and a top-notch flashlight. Plus you'll probably want a camera and binoculars as well. (Yes, these things can all be given away.) A big shelf of good books would help you learn more about the wildlife of Southern Africa, and fortunately many of them can be found in the A.U. library. But in case you have room in your carry-on luggage, we'll suggest a couple of field guides that you could mark up or tote out in the African rain. When we last checked, all were available through Amazon.com.

AMPHIBIANS. Chris and Ab would rather lose passports and malaria pills than be in Zimbabwe without Channing, A. 2001. *Amphibians of Central and Southern Africa.* Comstock/Cornell, Ithaca, New York, USA.

BIRDS. Of the many guides available, we are partial to Newman, K. 2002. *Birds of Southern Africa.* Struik, Cape Town RSA.

INSECTS. Unless you're a real entomologist, you will do best with Griffiths, C. 2004. *Field Guide to Insects of Southern Africa.* Struik, Cape Town, RSA.

MAMMALS. Mammal books have proliferated like *Mastomys natalensis*, and you really should check A.U.'s library holdings. But for a guide of your very own, you could try Stuart, C., and T. Stuart. 2007. *Field Guide to Mammals of South Africa.* Struik, Cape Town, RSA.

SCALY REPTILES. We'll recommend two; the second is a little better for snakes, but the first includes lizards, turtles, and crocs as well. These founts of herpetological information are Branch, B. 1998. *Field Guide to Snakes and Other Reptiles of Southern Africa.* Ralph Curtis Books, Sanibel Island, Florida, USA, and Marais, J. 2005. *Complete Guide to Snakes of Southern Africa.* Struik, Cape Town, RSA.

TAXONOMY. For any readers interested in more trendy classifications of amphibians (particularly frogs) and scaly reptiles, we would recommend Vitt, L., and J. Caldwell. 2009. *Herpetology: An Introductory Biology of Amphibians and Reptiles.* Elsevier/Academic Press, Amsterdam.

"If you can make two blades of grass grow where only one had grown before, then you will be of more significance than the whole race of politicians."

Fanuel Tagwira (2007 welcome to new Ag Students at A.U.)

food

chapter three

"I sing the goodness of the Lord, That filled the earth with food..."

Isaac Watts

For six thousand years farming has been the most human of all endeavors. The enterprise is our link to the life-giving energy of the sun, and our agriculture thereby provides the very molecules that fuel our blood. Developed through 300 human generations of experimental ecology, farming is the ultimate applied science, without which 99% of the world's people would starve. Farming keeps us alive.

A textbook narrative of a hypothetical farm might list a sequence of seasonal events — of suntimes and rains, of harvests and seedings, of slaughters and births. But the story of a real farm admits more profound cycles, which we ignorant ag-stat number-crunchers call Randomness. A real farm's story includes droughts and dust storms and rains of perfect generosity; a real farmer knows that expectation can lead to heartbreak and that despair can blossom into abundance. As the preacher's sermon text would say, the history of a real farm includes Pharaoh's seven fat years and his seven lean.

If the essence of a farm could be captured within definitions of climate, weather, soil type, cultivar, and technique, then agriculture would be a complex but manageable science. In actuality, however, no ag-system is independent from the wider world. This is true at both micro- and macro-scales. Viewed close up, the fate of a farm depends upon farm workers' efficiency, which reflects the level of their education, the health of their children, the content of their character, and the durability of their hope. The multi-system dependency of farming is also clear when viewed from a distance: the export of a farm's produce necessitates the replacement of soil nitrogen, so agricultural productivity is constrained by the price of fertilizer, which is a function of the cost of fossil fuels, which is bound to the liquidity of international capital and the fortunes of war. Even in America, where subsidies and crop insurance buffer the winds of disaster, farm-

ers know that they are impacted by social factors beyond their control. And in today's Africa the importance of intersystemic connections looms much larger. As an African farm child, you would imbibe with your mother's milk (or learn upon your first miracle-session at an Internet keyboard) the truth that historical forces — race and power and economics and violence — can be as capricious as the weather, and agriculturally as important. Furthermore, you would know that to hedge against these powerful factors you could invest only your sweat equity and your prayers.

In other words, the narrative of any real farm in modern Africa is a story of human striving that occurs at the intersection between biology and history. And A.U. runs a very real farm in very modern Africa. Sustained by the alluvial soils of the Mutare drainage, the University farming operation produces irrigated wheat, dryland corn/maize, and a number of less important crops. The farm also husbands goats, pigs, chickens (layers as well as broilers), tilapia, and dairy cattle. Through these productive enterprises the A.U. Farm fulfills three interrelated missions. First, it serves as a laboratory for courses in the Faculty of Agriculture. Second, it produces food, some for extramural sale and some for on-campus consumption; both distributions have proved particularly important during the recent years of Zimbabwe's political-economic crisis. Finally the farm provides employment for many farm workers and also serves as a safe haven for some of their families.

From the school's beginning, A.U.'s Farm has featured prominently in brochures, newsletters, and videos, and during every normal year since 1992 virtually all campus visitors have taken time to admire its productive operation. But recent years in Zimbabwe have

"Even if a farmer intends to loaf, he gets up in time to get an early start."

Edgar Watson Howe

Fig. 3.1: "Tractors for our Daily Bread" donation

not been normal, and during these difficult times the University's farm has taken on a deeper significance. In our chapters on campus geology and campus wildlife, we established the metaphor of Africa University as a lifeboat. And we believe that the A.U. Farm may be the most important lifeboat of all — with the largest and most significant crew.

By definition the crew of a properly operating lifeboat is heroic, and, essentially, the A.U. Farm operates properly. But the nature of a lifeboat is to be crowded, and if its voyage is protracted, even the best crew will inevitably confront the rise of stress. In the case of A.U.'s Farm, the effects of stress have been largely overcome by enormous reservoirs of strength, hope, and good humor. Nevertheless, in the voices of those who work the University's farm, we have heard both laughter and tension. Our intent is that we be faithful to both themes.

The two most difficult tensions involve pay and residence, and there is no way that either tension can be fully resolved. Most A.U. farm workers are very thankful for their jobs, but all these folks would like to make more money. This desire is not motivated by rampant greed. Food, school fees, and medical care are expensive; furthermore, in Zimbabwe's climate of hyperinflation, a salary that was munificent in August will be miniscule by October. Cost-of-living adjustments seem always to lag behind prices, and the nation's economy simply does not allow for the development of personal or family economic security. The United Methodist Church is not directly responsible for the farm salaries at A.U. Still, the church would like for the salaries to be higher, and we agree that improving the economic welfare of the farm workers is an idea whose time has come. But the church cannot simply print money: *de facto,* her total budget is set by the contributions she receives, and within that budget, priorities must be established. Furthermore, during America's economic "crisis" (a term that is ludicrous by Zimbabwean standards), United Methodist congregations in the USA have not always met their apportionments. The entire mission of the church, including the support of Africa University, has consequently suffered. So can the farm workers' salaries be raised? Of course they can. We just have to make that a higher priority, and we have to give more generously to support it.

In many respects the issue of residence is even more formidable than the problem of salaries. Most University farm workers have friends and loved ones who live elsewhere. Consequently, as conditions in Zimbabwe generally worsened, A.U. workers often wanted to bring these folks onto campus. And indeed many Zimbabweans visit acquaintances at the University, but these people cannot stay as long as some folks might like. Furthermore, as you will see, many employees are themselves unable to live on campus. This, for now, seems absolutely necessary. Africa University operates under Zimbabwean charter. The University is bound by the laws of the nation, and the nation's laws specify how many people may live on what farms under what conditions. This delicate matter is the subject of prayerful tension and careful negotiation among the church, farm workers, A.U. administrators, and officers of Zimbabwean law. In some ways this is a quintessential "lifeboat problem." And the authors of this book, who do not share the boat, are not competent to discuss it.

During each of our semesters at Old Mutare, we've enjoyed our proximity to the A.U. Farm. (Since all four authors are children of agricultural communities, we know that farming can be difficult, disappointing, and even dangerous for actual farmers. But for ecologists it's a fascinating spectator sport!) We have observed the farm's changes across seasons: the first green blades of wheat appear… rented combines crawl across the golden fields… small boys hunt spiny mice in the post-harvest stubble. We've also noted changes over the years.

Farm Managers come and go. The dairy emphasis shifts from Jersey cows to Holsteins. The little Ford tractors, donated out of Manhattan, Kansas (Fig. 3.1), are replaced with Massey Ferguson 440s, made in Brazil.

Our observations of change were important to us because they reinforced the fact that any real farm exists within history. And history rides roughshod over the seasonal changes so beloved by poets who have never farmed their way through a world recession or seven lean years of drought. Nevertheless, we have learned that on Africa University's farm, some things transcend history. Furthermore — since we are not ag-historians, and since in any case we have not seen enough of the farm to trace its history in detail — we have decided to focus this chapter on three things that change in specifics but abide in essence. These are the hopes, the dreams, and the honest labor of A.U.'s farm workers.

So, we do not recount for you the story of how the A.U. Farm developed; we do not catalog the data of its crop production, and we resist the temptation to map the distribution of its soil types. Instead, we present for you a collection of snapshots from a brief moment of history (all taken by G.R. Davis in December, 2007, all collapsed into one narrative day). By means of these photographs, we introduce you to some of A.U.'s farm workers, and we share with you some of the good things that they shared with us. In other words, we've paid our homage to the power of history; now let's get on with the important stuff. Let's follow G.R. to the farm and meet some real people!

A Journey to the Farm

In distance, the journey to the farm is not a long one. Starting out from Chris' and Ab's house, I take the major road leading toward the academic campus. During a regular semester, this road is heavily traveled by University buses transporting A.U. employees to work and by the automobiles of faculty, staff, and students rich enough to own them. Now, however, this close to Christmas I have the road almost to myself, and it is a fine day for walking. After about a kilometer, two roads diverge. Instead of veering right — to the classrooms, labs, and offices — I turn left on a narrower, muddier track (Fig. 3.8). This

road, and the network of paths and trails branching out from it, will take me to the buildings, animals, and people that comprise the A.U. Farm. And although the academic campus is largely deserted on this December day, the farm's employees are hard at work.

Fig 3.2: Preparing ground with hoe

Fig. 3.3: Planting maize

Fig. 3.4: Mr. Timothy Dozva

Fields and Crops

The first sight to greet me is a muddy field being hoed and planted by half a dozen women and men (Figs. 3.2 and 3.3). Supervisors Sarudzai Sadupwa, Irrigation Foreman, and Timothy Dozva, Field Foreman, explain that the recent rains have been so heavy that A.U.'s tractors can't work the fields. It is crucial that the maize be planted right away, so field workers have been busy, tilling by hand since 6:30 a.m. They'll have lunch (*sadza*) from 1-2 p.m. and are scheduled to finish this plot by 4:30 p.m.

Early this morning Crop Supervisor Robert Saugweme determined how much should be accomplished in a day's labor, and the field workers believe that if the rain holds off, they may even finish a little ahead of schedule today.

Conversing further with the two supervisors, I learn that both have housing on the A.U. campus. Timothy (Fig. 3.4) lives alone, apart from his two wives. His adult sons work in urban occupations in Bulawayo, Zimbabwe, and his daughters reside in Botswana. Sarudzai (Fig. 3.5) lives with his wife, who works at the Sales Point, and children, two of whom attend Hartzell School.

Not far beyond the maize-field-in-the-making, I notice a patch of shrub-like trees (Fig. 3.7). Some of them have been pruned today, and others have sprouted an abundance of small leaves. This is the Lokina Tree Project. It occupies about two hectares on the A.U. Farm, and Freddy Hunduza is its sole employee. He tells me that the trees' small leaves are harvested, dried for four days, ground up, and

Fig. 3.5: Mr. Sarudzai Sadupwa

added to cattle feed. This saves money by stretching the feed and also offers the cows better nutrition. But boosting leaf production requires frequent and severe pruning. Freddy is doing that job today (Fig. 3.6), and he is also responsible for picking leaves and weeding the plot. Although he works alone and doesn't take a lunch break, he says that he likes his job on the tree farm. Freddy has been assigned

Fig 3.7: Lokina Tree Project

Fig. 3.6: Mr. Freddy Hunduza pruning trees as Zephania Bonde looks on

Fig. 3.8: Road past "the Old Campus" (pre-A.U. Farm buildings temporarily used for classes and now returned to farm-related activities)

to this project for five years, having previously worked in the fields and in the farm's greenhouse. He lives with his wife and their three children (two boys ages 13 and 8 and a daughter age 5) in Tsingwe, about 3 km from the A.U. Farm. Because of an infection in his foot, Freddy moves slowly, and the walk takes him over an hour; he leaves home in time to arrive here by 6 a.m., and his workday ends at 4 p.m. He repeatedly insists that his injury does not interfere with his ability to do his job.

Across the road from the fields are the buildings of the former Hartzell Mission Farm (Fig. 3.8), which served as A.U.'s first academic campus. When Chris and Ab taught here in 1993, the buildings (previously the homes of hogs and chickens, or so the story goes) were classrooms, labs, faculty offices, a dining hall, and the Registrar's Office. Today they provide storage as well as homes for some of the farm workers. They also house the Sales Point, where A.U. employees can purchase eggs, yogurt, milk, chickens, and other farm produce as available.

Fig. 3.9: Mrs. Gladys Zimunya

Here I meet Gladys Zimunya, the Sales Supervisor (Fig. 3.9). Gladys, an aspiring bookkeeper, has been Sales Supervisor for three years, after working as sales clerk for three years. She was promoted following the arrest of her predecessor, who was caught falsifying the record books. Gladys likes her job and says it is challenging.

Gladys and her mechanic husband of six years live on the A.U. Farm in the residential complex (Fig. 3.31, near the end of this chapter) across from the Equipment Shed. They have two children, the older of whom lives with Gladys' mother-in-law and is doing well in school. Gladys sees this child every two weeks. The younger child is three months old and stays at home with Gladys' unmarried younger sister while Gladys is at work.

Close to Gladys' office is a newer farm structure, the greenhouse, which is constructed largely of unfinished lumber and sheet-plastic (Fig. 3.10). Here Margarit Ndakurirwa (Fig. 3.11) cares for the ornamental plants used to beautify the academic campus. Margarit has worked on the A.U. Farm for 10 years, starting with field crops and then assigned to the plant nursery for the past four years. She likes her present job better than work in the fields, in part because she now determines what needs to be done and then does it without excessive interference — thanks to a good supervisor who is not hard to please. She also likes working with vegetables, and next to the greenhouse she tends a small plot of tomatoes.

Margarit is a widow. Her six children, ranging in age from 5-18, stay with a cousin's wife in Marange, a distant rural area now rapidly developing because of diamond mines. She sees them once a month. Margarit herself lives rent-free on a small plot of land about an hour's walk from campus. She gets up at 6 a.m., skips breakfast, and arrives at work by 8 a.m. Her workday ends at 4:20 p.m.

Fig. 3.10: Greenhouse. The red brick building in the background is a student dormitory.

Fig. 3.11: Mrs. Margarit Ndakurirwa displays the hardiest greenhouse plant.

Chickens

If I should walk straight past the greenhouse and follow the main farm road maybe 50 meters beyond "the Old Campus" (Fig. 3.8), I'd come to a flooded field labeled "Kassina Pond" on this book's endpage maps. I suspect that Ab may drag me out there tonight, because at dusk on a day like today, the pond will explode into a mighty chorus of sex-crazed frogs. But my business during daylight hours is with the farm, so just short of the pond, I turn right and take a road that leads uphill to a scatter of buildings that house Africa University's livestock.

My first stop is the Chicken Layers House. Here I encounter Mary Makute, A.U.'s major employee in poultry production since 2003. In Fig. 3.14 Mary is "picking eggs." Earlier in the morning she had fed the birds a layers' mash that is specially formulated to increase productivity and assure shells strong enough to minimize breakage. The mash is made mostly from maize, but when feed is in short supply, grass will supplement the layers' diet. The chickens are kept in wire cages, which are suspended from the roof. Field workers periodically collect the manure that accumulates under the cages, and this is eventually applied as fertilizer to the farm fields. The layer chickens at the farm start producing at about 18 weeks of age; about a year later they'll "graduate" to the status of broilers. It's what academicians might call a terminal degree.

Fig. 3.12: Mrs. Mary Makute

Fig. 3.13: Mr. Joseph Kabera

Fig. 3.14: Mary Makute "picking" eggs

Mary likes her work at the Layers House. She says, "You learn a lot." And the birds have certainly learned to recognize her. I watch Mary walk the aisles between quiet cages as she picks the eggs. But when I join her to help, the birds become noisy and querulous. I ask what is happening. Mary replies, "The chickens are saying, 'Who is this?'" When we finish collecting the eggs, Mary wipes each one with a wet rag. Then she sorts them according to size and counts every egg, including the cracked ones. Mary keeps the tally on a large chalkboard hanging on the wall and also in a record book that security guards check daily. Meanwhile, the chickens have calmed. I ask Mary, "What are the chickens saying now?" She says that when they are content they quit talking and begin to sing.

Mary's days with the chickens start early. Skipping breakfast, she leaves home (3-4 km away) at 5 a.m. and walks to the Layers House where she works from 6 a.m. until 4 p.m. She brings a lunch of *sadza*, which she eats in the Layers House during the early afternoon. After seven consecutive days on the job, she has two days off, and each month she also gets a "Shopping Day." On the days Mary does not work, Joseph Kabera (Fig. 3.13), Livestock Specialist, takes over. Today Joseph also comments on the music the chickens make. I ask what they are singing. "A funny song only God knows," Joseph assures me. Zephania Bonde, my student translator, adds "I think they make a good choir." "Lots of altos!" I note.

Careful monitoring by security guards, day and night, underscores the value of the eggs and chickens under Mary's care. And during my visit she and Joseph tell me many tales about thievery by people and wildlife. Once a University student was caught leaving the Layers House wearing a large coat — under which security officers found 14 eggs. The student was arrested and disciplined by the University administration. Pythons, cobras, and feral cats threaten both the eggs and the chickens themselves. Mary recalled a python that had pulled four birds from their cage and eaten them. Security officers caught the python — it is bad luck to kill such a snake — and released it elsewhere on the A.U. property. Late one November night a security guard rousted Chris and Ab out of their house with the demand that they come apprehend an enormous cobra that was raiding the chickens. A mad dash through the mud and rain revealed chickens still squawking with fear (or indignation), but the cobra had long since made its escape.

Most of the layers survive these sundry depredations and are processed as broilers at about 72 weeks of age. After leaving Mary and Joseph, I encounter two workers (Joel Nyabunze, Manager of Broiler Chickens and Piggery Foreman, and Adam Nhiwatiwa) who are butchering broilers for an end-of-semester faculty celebration. In Figure 3.15, Joel stuffs the feet into the body cavities before he and Adam package the freshly slaughtered broilers for delivery to the academic campus. At A.U., no part of the bird is thrown away. The intestines and the heads will provide food for the people who help with the butchering. Allocation of chicken parts is a serious business; indeed one employee was terminated because she got into a fight with a co-worker over who would keep the heads.

Pigs

Up the road from the Layers House is the piggery, where Joel and Adam spend their workday when they are not slaughtering broilers. Joel is a long-term A.U. employee, having worked at the farm since 1993. He is an expert in the husbandry of pigs and poultry. In addition to 14 years of on-the-job experience, he completed a correspondence course and then an on-site Practical with the Pig Industry Board; he has also taken formal coursework on Broilers and Layers.

Joel hails from the Rusape area, where his family still lives. Each Monday his wife visits and picks up his pay to help support their three children and Joel's mother, who lives with them. Joel himself stays on the A.U. Farm. This allows him to check on the pigs and chickens at night.

As Foreman, Joel is responsible for record-keeping at the piggery (Fig. 3.16). Each page in his book — which security guards check every day — lists details for a separate litter of pigs. These include the ID numbers of the parental boar and sow, the birth weight of each piglet, and a record of its weight gains. Joel also keeps records in his head, remembering and reciting for me the birth dates of all the piglets under his charge.

Fig. 3.15: Mr. Joel Nyabunze processing broilers

Fig. 3.16: Later, Joel explains the records kept on pigs.

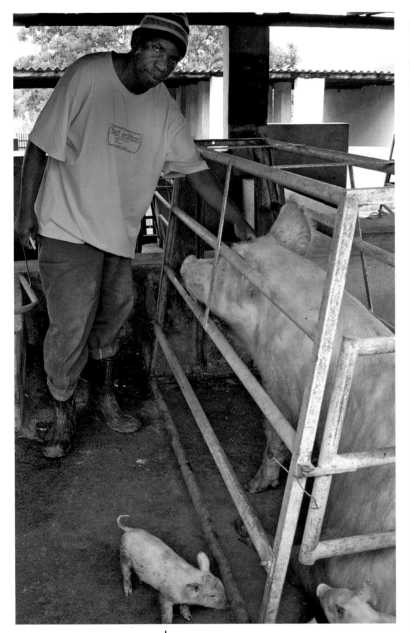

Fig 3.17: Caging of sow and piglets

Fig 3.18: Mr. Adam Nhiwatiwa hoses down a pig.

One of Joel's least-favorite duties is the processing of newborn pigs. First he pulls the piglet's teeth with pliers, and then he cuts a unique pattern of notches into the ears to identify each animal. Injection of an iron solution compensates for blood lost through these procedures. After processing, the piglets are returned to Mom, who is confined by a stout metal cage that prevents her from accidentally trampling her offspring (Fig. 3.17)

Fig. 3.19: Joel and the heir-apparent breeder-boar

Joel takes great pleasure in touring me through the breeder-hogs' barn. Along the way he shows me several sows that have recently been serviced by a big boar now recuperating in a pen of his own. When we reach the young boar shown in Figure 3.19, Joel explains that after the older male is retired, this young animal will assume his duties. "That pig has a bright future" I remark. Joel agrees heartily.

Adam Nhiwatiwa, Joel's assistant and washer of pigs and piggery (Fig. 3.18), also grew up near Rusape. He now lives with his wife, son, and daughter in a rental house in Tsingwe, about 3 km from the A.U. Farm. Adam makes the walk to work six days a week, arriving at the piggery at 6 a.m. and leaving at 4 p.m. Like Mary, he gets the customary Shopping Day each month. Adam would like to live closer to A.U. but cannot afford the rent.

Dairy Cattle

Around a curve in the road and beyond smell-distance from the piggery, I reach the dairy barn and adjacent pasture, where the farm's largest animals reside. During the early years of A.U., compact Jer-sey cows were all the fashion. Nowadays, however, big, heavy Holsteins are preferred, and today some of them appear less than contented. Perhaps that's because in December of 2007, livestock feed is in short supply. On the day of my visit, two A.U. Farm trucks have been stranded in Harare for over 48 hours, waiting to load five tons of feed for the cows, pigs, and chickens. Short term, the cows can be let loose on the farm property to graze. But modern dairy cows don't make much milk on grass, so production is down dramatically, and everyone is concerned about how the livestock will be sustained over the Christmas holiday. Farm staff estimates that 25 tons of feed will be needed during that interval. Fully loaded, an A.U. truck can carry two and a half tons, so that's 10 round trips to the Grain Board supply point in Harare — and the first trips are not going well. Additional supplies should be available in the New Year, but for now the situation appears bleak.

Even if they're subsisting mostly on grass, dairy cows still require twice-daily milking, and milk must be processed as soon as it is collected. Sheme Mutsingo (Fig. 3.20) and Norman Dozva (Fig. 3.21) are the men who do this work, milking at 5 a.m. and again at 4 p.m. They then weigh the milk, (Fig. 3.22), record the production by each cow, and transfer the milk to storage containers (Fig. 3.23).

Norman and Sheme use their break time from 11 a.m. until 3 p.m. to work in their own fields, where they grow maize and vegetables. Cows are not seasonal, and so dairy workers never get a long vacation. They work seven days in a row, have two days off, and get a Shopping Day at the end of the month.

While Norman milks and weighs, Sheme talks to me about himself and his family. Born in 1972, Sheme started his career at the A.U. Farm in its very first year (1992), working in the fields. He and his wife have two boys and two girls: the older two children are already in school at the Hartzell Mission, but the baby is only 20 months old. I

Fig. 3.20: Mr. Sheme Mutsingo, dairyman

Fig. 3.21: Mr. Norman Dozva milking

Fig. 3.22: Weighing milk

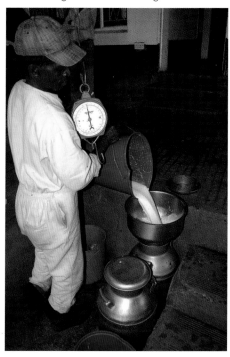
Fig. 3.23: Transferring milk

ask Sheme if he got a day off from milking when his youngest child was born. He laughs and says that he left his wife at Old Mutare Hospital on his way to work — and following the afternoon milking, he stopped by the hospital "to see what had happened."

Today the Mutsingo family lives on the campus farm in the residential complex near the equipment shed (Fig. 3.31). Sheme likes living so close to his work, and he doesn't exactly worry about rent because the charges are automatically deducted from his salary. Although their quarters sometimes have electricity, the Mutsingos do not own an electric stove "because there is never money to buy one."

Even for those workers who might buy a stove, electricity in the troubled Zimbabwe of 2007 is a chancy proposition. Ab tells me that he seldom had power from late August through September. At the time of my visit, electrical service to A.U.'s campus and farm is fairly reliable, reportedly because the University was served by the same line as a profitable nearby gold mine. But this could change at any time. (Indeed, since the mine's closure late in 2008, the University and its farm have become increasingly dependent on its diesel generators, which are often run for only a few hours a day.) Besides inconveniencing families, interruptions in electrical service put the A.U. milk supply at risk since coolers and heaters rely upon electricity.

Auxiliary Farm Activities

Most of the people I meet during my journey to the farm work directly with plants, animals, or their products at specifically defined job locations. However, I also encounter several farm employees whose duties involve machinery, supplies, or security rather than livestock or crops. These people are typically not tied to one set of buildings or fields; instead, they traverse the entire farm.

One such worker is Frank Chazuka, Stores Clerk (Fig. 3.24). Having held the position for 10 years, he says his responsibility is "to order goods needed on the farm, to keep them, then to distribute them to the different enterprises." These goods include everything from irrigation pipe (Fig. 3.24) to seed and fertilizer (Fig. 3.25).

Frank is good with the books, making excellent use of his O-Level education, but he likes big equipment and hopes someday to get into the transportation business. Frank's family, a wife and two children, live with him and with other families in the residential complex across from the A.U. Equipment Shed.

Another mobile farm worker is tractor driver and electrician Elisha Chitsamba (Fig. 3.26). Elisha worked in the fields for three years before his supervisor decided he should be a tractor driver, and "that promotion made me very happy." On the day that I visit, the fields are too wet for tractors, so Elisha and his Massey Ferguson are making deliveries to the Sales Point and the University Dining Hall.

Elisha picked up his electrical skills during an informal six-month apprenticeship with the senior electrician on the A.U. campus. He tells me that his training was very hands-on, and he describes the time when he was reattaching connections at the bore pump (for one of three deep wells that provide potable water for Africa University). Elisha touched a naked wire carrying 60 amps and was knocked down for several seconds. He says with a smile, "From that time I learned a lot!" Elisha lives with his wife, their three daughters, and one son in the complex by the Equipment Shed.

Security guards have perhaps the most varied jobs on the A.U. Farm. Joel Mudada (Fig. 3.27), Security Supervisor, oversees two foremen and 12 guards, one of whom is John Mark Ziwha, introduced to you in Chapter 1. Joel establishes duties and schedules for each guard on a daily basis; he also works the shift opposite his corporal and is on call 24 hours each day. According to Joel, "inside theft" (that is, theft by A.U. employees) is the biggest day-shift problem. Eggs, milk, grain, mealies, fertilizer, seeds, diesel fuel, and even tractors are potentially vulnerable. "Outside theft" is also a problem and may be particularly serious at night.

Security guards work 12 hour shifts, starting at either 6 a.m. or 6 p.m. Guards who write well are usually assigned to the day shift because more recordkeeping is required during this period. To ensure the integrity of the security force, night guards never know where they'll be assigned until they report for duty, and all personnel are instructed to avoid close friendships with farm workers. Providing security for the A.U. Farm is especially challenging because the area is extensive, and only one guard is on duty during daylight hours. Also, guards do not have vehicles, radios, or firearms.

Joel began his career in security when he was 32 years old, training in 1996 with Guard Alert, a commercial security institute. Although

Fig. 3.25: Seed and fertilizer

Fig. 3.24: Mr. Frank Chazuka and some of his stores

he likes his job, he often feels isolated because he must monitor every aspect of security for the A.U. Farm. This includes checking on his fellow supervisors, with whom he cannot become too friendly.

Joel's family life proves as interesting to me as his job. I learn that he has six children, ranging in age from 6-12 — and two wives. I ask Joel if having two wives is an indication of wealth or power. He replies that his father, who was neither rich nor influential, also had two wives. Joel recognizes that polygamy is becoming less common in modern-day Zimbabwe, but he sees nothing unusual about the practice. He currently lives with one of his wives on the A.U. campus. I do not inquire about his allocation of time or resources.

Since I've talked a lot about farm security, I also want you to meet the day's duty guard. Today this is Edward Gungutsava (Fig. 3.28), who has one wife, two teenage sons, and two teenage daughters. Edward usually works day shifts because he is good with reports, and this year he'll be on duty from 6 a.m. to 6 p.m. on Christmas, though he'll have Boxing Day (26 December) off.

Farm Workers at Home

As I talk with more and more people, I am increasingly impressed by the diversity of farm employees' living arrangements. Some workers stay with their families in nearby villages and rise before dawn each morning for the walk to A.U. Other employees rent a room in Old Mutare or Tsingwe; they live apart from spouse(s) and children, seeing them only once or twice a month. I am repeatedly told that on-campus housing, when available, is the preferred option because residents can live with their families and also be close to their work. Although I'd never invite myself into somebody

Fig. 3.26: Mr. Elisha Chitsamba

Fig. 3.27: Mr. Joel Mudada, Security Supervisor

Fig. 3.28: Mr. Edward Gungutsava checks record books.

else's house, I am quite curious about the farm's family quarters and am delighted when two men ask me to visit their homes.

I first meet Tongesai Mungwari at milking time. He is visiting dairymen Norman and Sheme, his friends and former coworkers. Tongesai has an interesting story to tell. After working with A.U.'s pigs, broilers, and layers for nine years, he tried to establish a farm of his own. Despite his vast experience, "the project failed completely." So, Tongesai did what thousands of black Africans have had to do since the time of Cecil Rhodes: he left his family and crossed a national border, looking for work.

Today he manages sheep and chickens on a farm near Johannesburg, where the pay is decent even though foreign workers are not really welcomed. Meanwhile his wife maintains a homebase in Zimbabwe, and Tongesayi works four months straight to accumulate 20 days' leave for visiting his family at A.U. Twenty months' work in South Africa, with infrequent visits home, has enabled him to send packages of sugar and other supplies to his family and parents.

After relating his story Tongesayi invites me to meet his family, saying "A small house with a large welcome." Indeed it is both!

The Mungwari family occupies two small, cluttered rooms behind the Old Campus of Africa University. There are two beds, one for Tongesayi and wife Linda, the other for their three children, a baby son and two older daughters. Linda Mungwari (Fig. 3.29) works at the A. U. Stores; she also tends a garden, of which her husband is justly proud, and she cares for the children.

As a 37-year-old father with a hard job in unfriendly territory a long way from home, Tongesayi feels the weight of many responsibilities. Considering the stress in his life, I bluntly ask the man why he doesn't just give up. He responds with a Shona parable and assures me that he will most definitely hang on. This hold-fast philosophy also underlies Tongesavi's sense of patriotism. He feels a strong bond to Zimbabwe and will make a special trip from South Africa to vote in the upcoming elections (29 March 2008). This sentiment is shared by many other Zimbabweans, who are deeply troubled by the economic situation but who love their country too much to abandon it.

My second home visit takes place in the farm housing complex — seven families in a long brick building across from the Equipment Shed. I'm here to see the family of Crop Supervisor Robert Soungweme (Fig. 3.31). As one of five supervisors who report directly to the farm manager, Robert is in the second line of command on the A.U. Farm. As a senior supervisor, he establishes the duties for workers in crops and has the authority to appoint and dismiss even foremen, with the approval of the farm manager. According to Robert, "supervisors see that the activities are carried out in the proper way they should be carried out as prescribed by the manager. It is the supervisor's duty to prescribe to foremen what is to be done and to make the plans and propose those plans to the farm manager for approval." In his area, Robert will "insist on following the principles of agriculture. No shortcuts. Use the right amount of seeds, fertilizer. Procedures must be followed exactly as prescribed by agricultural principles."

Robert served as security supervisor from 1992-1995; he was livestock supervisor from 1995-2000 and has been crop/field supervisor since 2002. His professional credentials include certificates in

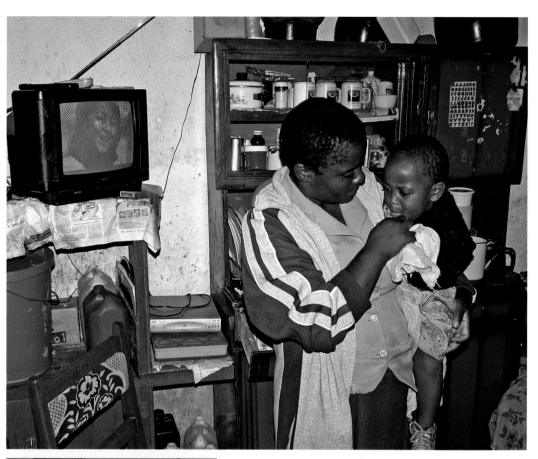

Fig. 3.29: Mrs. Linda Mungwari and son

Fig. 3.30: Mr. Tongesayi Mungwari and his son

Fig. 3.31: Crop Supervisor Mr. Robert Soungweme shows off one of the guinea pigs his family raises as food. The farm workers' housing complex is directly behind Robert, and the Equipment Shed is to the far right.

piggery and broilers, and he is currently working on an Advanced Crop Husbandry Certificate via distance education at the Polytechnic Institute. He takes tests on a monthly basis and will travel to Harare "to write the final examination." I ask if he will be nervous, but Robert emphatically denies that possibility: "No, I will not be nervous because I know that someone will be taking care of me." He allows me to interpret this statement as an expression of religious faith.

In our initial conversations Robert's favorite words seem to be "prescribed" and "whereby" and "procedures," so I suspect that the man is difficult to please and may be seriously lacking in human warmth. I am wrong — at least about the warmth. Once we begin talking about family, and as he shows me around his home, I come to admire Robert and to consider him a strong friend. I also discover that he has quite a sense of humor.

Robert speaks so assertively and with such authority that when he tells me he has 18 wives, I try not to overreact. After all, Timothy Dozva and Joel Mudada have two wives, and some men in Zimbabwe probably have even more. But 18? As I open my journal to record this startling information, Robert breaks into a wide grin: the white American has just proved to be as gullible as he looks. Secretly I am relieved to discover that Robert has a sense of humor, but if any man could manage 18 wives, Robert Soungweme would be that man!

Robert has but one wife, who works part time at a phone shop. Together they have four children, two of whom live at home (Fig. 3.32). The youngest is five-year-old Tadiwanashe, in the red shirt; Tafadzwa, age 11, is to the left of her father.

Both parents have high expectations for their children, and their children do very well in school. At his wife's urging Robert searches through a cabinet and produces the most recent report card of his 15-year-old son, Leondwens. In his class of 47 students at Mutare Boys High School, Leondwens ranks tenth in agriculture, seventh in history, seventh in Shona, sixth in integrated science, fourth in English, third in geography, second in mathematics, and first in commerce.

Eleven-year-old Tafudzwa is also quite the scholar, and she proudly poses with her stellar report card (Fig. 3.35). Although you

Fig. 3.32: The Soungweme family at home

Fig. 3.33: Mrs. Soungweme and her electric stove

cannot see her grades and rankings in the picture, have no doubt that they rival those of her older brother.

As a Senior Supervisor, Robert can afford the rent on a multi-room home, and he has also been able to buy a number of modern appliances, including a two-burner hot plate (Fig. 3.33). Other farm families, lacking electricity or the money for stoves, cook over firewood in outdoor kitchens (Fig. 3.34). The Soungwemes also use this method when electric power goes down.

Of course, cooking on an open fire means that someone must collect the wood, and A.U. Farm residents often send out their children to do this chore (Fig. 3.36). As we noted in this book's Creatures chapter, the harvest of firewood is a serious environmental issue, both in the university wildlands and in Zimbabwe more generally. Although a substantial amount of wood is gathered for on-campus use, my impression is that most of the big-tree damage is done by outsiders who leave piles of branches and trunks for pick up in the dark of night (by contrast, note the modest diameters of the stems in Figure 3.36).

Hopes and Dreams

Since its earliest history, Africa University has invoked the "dream" theme, a motif that is frequently used in soliciting donations ("support the Dream"), in identifying special projects ("the Dream Farm"), and in naming the campus infrastructure ("the Bridge to Dreams"). The farm workers I meet in my short stay also have hopes and dreams, some of them practical and short term but others substantially deferred and less tangible.

Because I am visiting the farm shortly before the December holidays, I ask several of the workers about their plans and wishes for Christmas. Joseph Kabera, the Livestock Specialist in the Layers House, describes in some detail the Christmas he envisions. He and his family will go to church at 10 a.m. Then they'll come home to spend the rest of the day listening to music on the radio, dancing, and "doing funny things to make the children laugh." He also wants to spend some time visiting with friends and "sharing ideas with people." Joseph adds that what his boys want for Christmas is a good meal of chicken and rice. "Having chicken to eat for Christmas would be very good!" he says excitedly. His wife would like a Coca-Cola and a Fanta. For himself, he'd like a new pair of shoes.

Many of the farm workers I meet hope for higher wages — if not by Christmas then at least someday. Like farmers in many other parts

Fig. 3.34: Outdoor kitchen

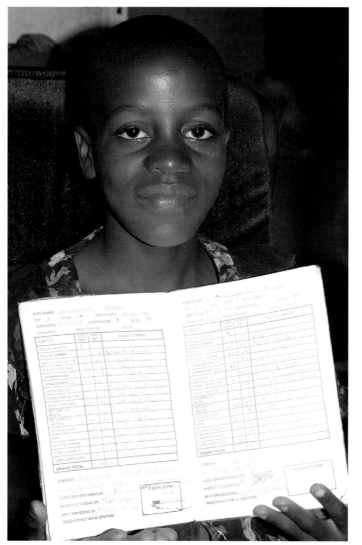

Fig. 3.35: Tafudzwa Soungweme takes pride in her report card.

Fig. 3.36: A.U. Farm children collecting firewood

of the world, A.U.'s agricultural employees receive pay that is miniscule in comparison to the value of the foodstuffs they produce. To cite one example, each tray of 30 eggs Mary Makute picks and packs in the Layers House could (depending in part on inflation and timing) represent more than six months of her pay. Other workers would like to see improvements in conditions of service. For example, Margarit, the Greenhouse Curator, wishes that farm employees would be provided with gum boots and protective clothing. And, of course, many workers would like to find on-campus housing for their families.

So, some workers dream of money, some of housing, some of simple things like chicken dinners or new gum boots. But in my conversations on the farm, the dreams most frequently reported involve obtaining qualifications for more responsible positions. Zimbabwe is a country justly proud of its educational system: its adult literacy rate of 89.4% is the highest in southern Africa. As a corollary of this pride, many occupations in Zimbabwe require formal certification (typically a diploma obtained through correspondence courses plus attendance at polytechnic institutes), and certification is always verified by rigorous, standardized exams. I have already listed the certificates held by A.U. employees in supervisory positions. Both these supervisors and their subordinates typically aspire to earn more such credentials.

Gladys, the Sales Point Manager, hopes to become an A.U. Farm bookkeeper within five years. To achieve that goal she'll need an accounting diploma. Piggery Foreman Joel has already received his certificate from the Pig Industry Board and has finished his coursework in broilers and layers. Once he completes a practical in Animal Health, he hopes to work in an academic lab at the University. Tractor driver and apprentice electrician Elisha would like to get his Electrical Workers Diploma, a certification that will require attending Saturday classes at Mutare Polytechnic Institute from January through December. Both Joel and Elisha intend to get their driving licenses soon, though this can be quite an ordeal in Zimbabwe. Frank, the Stores Manager, wants to obtain a Class 1 driver's license and then begin driving a bus or lorry. One day he hopes to own a transportation business.

As I have already emphasized, the A.U. farm workers also hold high educational aspirations for their children, and a good report card is a source of pride for the whole family. Sending children to school in Zimbabwe today requires significant sacrifices by many parents. School fees plus books and a uniform for even one child can require up to 20% of the wages of a nonsupervisory farm worker. And, for a family with four or five children, perhaps the only hope lies in the generosity of a broader community. These hard facts come home to me as I look across half a kilometer of Africa to A.U.'s academic campus. And I wonder how many sacrifices, how much generosity, may be required to secure a university education here on this continent.

Processing

In distance, the journey from the farm back to Faculty Row is not a long one. And during my week in Africa, I actually make it several times. At the end of each day on the farm, I retrace my steps along a dirt track to the muddy asphalt road that passes between the newly planted fields and the gray-white farm buildings where the University's first classes were held. Each day, more faces are familiar to me — Mary returning from the Layers House, Elisha on his big 440 tractor — and children wave to me with as much recognition as curiosity. At the campus' main drive, I turn right on clean pavement, toward my temporary home, toward the highways that will lead me back to America. I turn from the farm, but I remember.

Each day on the farm I take a lot of pictures: sometimes, indeed, I take hundreds; after all, in this Digital Age, I'm just rearranging electrons on a tiny memory card. When I get back to the house that Chris and Ab used for a semester, I'll crank up a laptop computer (I don't have a tech-school certificate in computer technology, but I think I can manage it anyhow) and download my photographs of pigs and chickens and irrigation pipes and children's report cards. Some of the pictures I'll delete immediately, but most I'll copy into computer folders that I'll label with phrases or names from my field notebook. I call this activity "processing," and I have to accomplish it quickly, or I'll lose touch with what my electronic images are all about. But there is also another kind of processing, and it does not happen in a single hour on a borrowed laptop. This is the processing of hopes and dreams and friendships that have been offered to me as gifts across a profound divide of race and culture and economic status. This is the processing of our time in Africa.

Africa, we have been told, imprints her images upon each person who visits her, rearranging, as it were, electrons in some memory-card of the brain. And in this book your four authors have attempted to process some of our images to share with you. Our chapters — and to a degree our concerns — have been very different: maps of geology, pictures of frogs, tales of Christmas wishes. But still, all our images are African: African people, landscapes, and creatures, recorded under an African sky, with the sound of an *mbira* in the background and the smell of rain upon the summer wind. We must not presume to tell you how you should reprocess the second-hand images that you have received from us. But remember: each includes a bit of love — and perhaps a smudge of red earth that should not wash away too easily.

"We sit still.
We lose ourselves in a pile
of leaves or its memory.
We listen and breezes from a
whole other world begin
to whisper."

James Carroll

117

partnerships

Wofford Professor Terry Ferguson and A.U. Security Guard / Sage John Mark Zihwa

"For a healing of the nations, Lord, we pray with one accord;
For a just and equal sharing of the things that earth affords;
To a life of love in action help us rise and pledge our word...."
Fred Kaan (Hymn 428)

"If you can make two blades of grass grow where only one had grown before...."
Fanuel Tagwira (2007 welcome to new Ag Students at A.U.)

On Wednesday, 11 March, 2009, ABC Nightly News finally showed America a Zimbabwe story that told more about the future than the past. Hidden among reports of medical emergencies and political crises was the fantastic news that Zimbabwe's elementary schools were back in session. Twenty bright-scrubbed children, their faded uniforms newly pressed, crowded into a fresh-swept classroom dominated by an enormous blackboard and a flag of their country. There was no electricity, books were in short supply, and one little boy had to bring a desk from home, but every child was smiling. Meanwhile, a tall, thin teacher in his dark coat and tie tried to scowl about the classes his pupils had missed, but a grin soon broke through. School was in session again, so Zimbabwe was really Zimbabwe, and that's all there was to it.

Chris and Ab repeatedly watched the news clip during the weekend that followed, and we had no difficulty imagining every kid eventually coming to A.U.: the little girl with the sunhat would be studying Wildlife, and the boy with the Bill Clinton twinkle would be running for student-body president. Zimbabwe is like that, once you get to know her: every sunrise warms a dream that transcends whatever tragedies the day might bring, and every little child in her school uniform invites you to invent a partnership that will endure into better tomorrows.

The book you have just read describes a place where people have been forging partnerships for more than 15 years. These are partnerships between friends, between farmers and their land, between students and their teachers, between citizens of two dozen African nations, between two continents separated by three centuries of turbulent history, between four South Carolina scientists who decided to write a book. And during the hectic weeks when we were finishing up this work, some of our American colleagues told us that we should conclude the volume with a plea for big-dollar gifts that might "help save Africa University." To us this suggestion seemed as quaint as the missionary hymns we'd sung in the days of our childhood — "From Greenland's Icy Mountains...." Probably that was because whatever small gifts we've offered to A.U. have been overshadowed by big gifts from A.U. to us. Where else could you see a pangolin, learn about *sadza*, and teach a Rwandan genius who would reinvent the calculus? Anyhow, for various reasons, the four of us will all say "No" to the recommendation that we become writers-mendicant. Instead, we'll suggest a consideration of partnership. This means that your four authors will share with you our ongoing struggles to maintain our stewardship connections with Africa University. We'll tell you what we're trying to do, and we'll suggest more specifically how you might be able to go beyond our modest efforts.

Our A.U. Ideas and Plans

Toward the end of our 2007 pilgrimages in Africa, we all were asked, more or less officially, about our recommendations for stewardship of A.U.'s campus resources. Initially we answered with our litany of woes — you've heard that sad tune again and again — and for a time everybody was comfortably depressed about desperate miners, vanishing species, and inflation-whipped farm workers. However, Professor Tagwira was unwilling to let matters rest in that state of contented resignation: "But we have shared our campus with you, and we really thought you'd want to be our partners in figuring out how to make it a better place." Eventually we stammered into the beginning of an answer: we told "Prof" three ideas about increasing the impact of conscientious stewardship on the Africa University campus. For you readers, we shall first define these ideas in very general terms. Then, as an example of what we mean, we'll focus more specifically on issues of wildlands conservation. Within this discussion we'll include four partnership-opportunity topics suggesting how you might join forces with the ongoing enterprise of Africa University. We'll even swallow our pride and write a little about sharing money, just in case that's a sort of partnership that seems appropriate to you.

PERSONAL COMMITMENT. Saint Francis talked about the ministry of the possible, and we bow to his wisdom. So, the four of us agree that every friend of A.U. should pledge to do, for sure, some small service for the University. That's why we wrote this book; that's why we shall donate all profits, however small, to A.U. For your part, you readers have already demonstrated your personal commitment by investing time and perhaps money to learn about Africa University. (Ab hopes that you'll see the book's movie-version too, which we assume will star Johnny Depp as adventure-photographer G.R. Davis.) You can follow up this commitment by offering prayers or perhaps even donations through the United Methodist Church.

A.U. HELPS A.U. Africa University is not a weak reed blowing in the harsh winds of a backwards country. It is a strong, vibrant institution in a nation as committed to education as any in the world. Therefore, we can reasonably expect that the major impetus for addressing institutional needs will come from within the institution! Despite our intimate contact with A.U., we remain to some degree outsiders, and it would be presumptuous for us to specify an Americans-know-best "do-list." Still, we can express our general conviction. The fundamental mission of A.U. is to serve Africa, and therefore the University should try to approach every on-campus "problem" as an opportunity for learning how to fulfill this mission. For example, although we are not development theorists, we can envision the University farm as a venue for designing agricultural projects based on norms of social justice and ecological sustainability. Without precise definition, those high-sounding words are no better than platitudes, but creative minds and willing hands (and A.U. has many of both) could translate this ivory-tower jargon into a seeds-in-the-ground reality. We realize that programs involving farm workers and students and teachers could become difficult and even contentious, but the business of a church institution is to deal graciously with difficulty and contention. We also recognize the hard fact that significant programs often carry significant monetary costs — and that, for now, the big bucks may need to come from extramural sources, from outside help.

Partnership Opportunity: Learning and Teaching

When you looked at our book, you took a step into partnership with Africa University. Now we hope you'll want to learn more — and also to teach other people what you are learning. The number of books about Africa is enormous, and many of these publications contain insights of potential importance to friends of A.U. Because of our particular academic backgrounds, our personal libraries are biased towards ecology and natural history. However, we trust that many of you readers have more balanced tastes in reading material. One excellent partnership project would be to develop an annotated bibliography of works that bear directly on Africa University. College students could begin this work in connection with an African history or contemporary-issues course. Pastors or Sunday School teachers could design reading lists for VIM teams or mission-studies. The best books and articles could be reviewed in Internet blogs or could serve as selections for community book clubs. And people who managed to visit A.U. could report on which readings actually proved most useful.

Partnership Opportunity: Scholarships

One thing we've learned about giving money in developing nations is that we are relatively ignorant about the most efficient way to allocate our partnership dollars. If you share our ignorance, and if you want to donate towards the academic program of Africa University, you can probably do no better than to send your dollars to the A.U. Development Office in Nashville. Nevertheless, over the course of our several visits to Zimbabwe, we have observed an increasing need for scholarship money. (By contrast, raising funds for brick-and-mortar projects such as chapels, classrooms, and even laboratories appears to be much easier.)

These students in Ab's Wildlife Ecology Class (October 2007) are practicing a first lesson in radio telemetry. For various reasons four of these five young men were able to able to obtain first-year scholarships to the Faculty of Agriculture and Natural Resources. Without these scholarships, none of the four would have been able to attend Africa University.

Because the University strives to make the most of its scholarship dollars, Zimbabwean students are usually expected to pay their own tuition during their first year and to prove themselves academically worthy of financial assistance for years two and three. Unfortunately this sensible policy sometimes prevents talented but poor high school graduates from having any chance to compete for eventual scholarships: they just can't possibly afford year one! Because many of the best potential agriculture students come from rural (and therefore very poor) backgrounds, limitations on first-year scholarships

hit particularly hard in the Faculty of Agriculture and Natural Resources. We'd love to see these farm kids (especially, perhaps, from the A.U. Farm) have the chance to study scientific agriculture. Dedicated scholarships would help.

Scholarships to A.U. are not cheap, but they are a very direct way that an individual — or perhaps a church or school group — could establish partnerships in the development of Southern Africa.

120

OUTSIDE HELP. If we really knew anything about raising money, Wofford and the College of Charleston would be paying us munificent salaries to court potential mega-donors. Furthermore, A.U. already has a superb development office (this book's movie version will also star Denzel Washington as Dr. Jim Salley and Halle Berry as Executive Secretary Glorianna McClain) with a coherent, long-term strategy. Still, maybe the friends of Africa University should try some long-shot gambles. For instance, can any of you readers figure a way to fling a load of white-liberal guilt on a rich former American President who let Rwanda, 1994, happen on his watch?

THE WILDLANDS CONTEXT. This is our specific-examples arena. We actually have some academic expertise in the field, so we can offer somewhat more definite ideas.

1. Wildlands conservation: Personal commitment. Chris and Ab plan to go back and teach for A.U.'s ag faculty during the first half of 2010. If Internet connections permit, we'll send reports, suggestions, tall tales, and photographs to South Carolina, where these items will be assembled into a website managed out of the Wofford Biology Department by G.R. and Terry. The website could also provide a venue for processing feedback from you readers. All four authors, along with Doctor Salley and Vice Chancellor Tagwira, will also take a hard look at any stewardship suggestions you might offer, and we'll work to make sure that any donations you might give are used wisely. In addition, Chris and Ab plan to sell a few priceless antiques (= unwanted junk), and if we can merchandise them to discriminating collectors (= suckers with money), we'll pay for a real taxonomist to visit A.U. and help with the ongoing faunal inventory. Is anybody looking for a....

2. Wildlands conservation: A.U. helps A.U. If we want to develop a world-class resource-management program for Africa University, then we must stop thinking about campus

Partnership Opportunity: Helping Farm Workers and Other Locals

This will be the most challenging partnership to develop, and yet it could be the most rewarding. Americans who visit A.U.'s campus are, in comparison to most Zimbabweans, incredibly rich. The University has been vigilant that a campus culture of begging should not develop, and visitors must not undercut this legitimate concern by thoughtless, feel-good gifts. On the other hand, there is an important difference between tossing throw-away dollars or safari clothing to someone you do not know — and starting a real friendship that manifests itself in part through the sharing of gifts. And if one could learn the real needs of a community and respond to those needs, such would be a partnership indeed.

If you visit Africa University, the chaplain's office could put you in touch with on-campus student groups concerned with service within the broader community. Your conversation, gifts, and ideas could help empower such organizations more fully; at the same time you would make new friends and have significant discussions with interesting students. On the other hand, if you need to establish your partnership from a trans-oceanic distance, then a phone call or email to the A.U. development office in Nashville could be a first step in that direction.

When we talk to University officials, we take the time to remind these good people of our abiding concern for the welfare of workers on the A.U. Farm. Also, we sometimes inquire whether a particular farm family might have some immediate need that could be met with a one-time donation. Over the years we have discovered that school fees and elementary school uniforms are in chronic short supply, and we wonder whether some creative American congregation might establish a partnership with an A.U. student group to address these issues.

exploitation as a curse — because it is actually a blessing. First, the campus is feeding people who would otherwise be hungry (or worse); if the "lifeboat" is overcrowded, at least it's keeping some souls afloat, for now. Second, the specific plight of A.U.'s campus is the general plight of modern Africa's natural-resource world. And the full name of A.U.'s Ag School is the Faculty of Agriculture and Natural Resources (FANR). Associated with this school are a score of First Team research scientists and a hundred very bright students. They have a 600-hectare laboratory upon which they can study in real time the exact resource issues that will bedevil Africa (indeed, the entire world) for the next hundred years. Bishop Hartzell could not have wished for more. Indeed, John Wesley himself — who said "the world is my parish" — could not have planned a more authentic service-laboratory experience because the local "parish" of FANR is, in microcosm, the entire world!

Furthermore, at A.U., FANR is not alone. Humanities and Social Sciences offers an excellent course in resource issues. Theology is crammed with teachers and students who are prepared to confront the issues of sharing and stewardship, even with fasting and prayer if necessary. Faculties of Management and of Health Sciences can broaden FANR's research and community service perspectives, and the mission of the Faculty of Education is outreach into the wider community. As a coursework or ser-

Partnership Opportunity: Fieldtrips

Almost every American visitor to southern Africa manages to view one of the region's fabulous national parks, and that is as it should be! On the other hand, only a relatively small percentage of Zimbabwe's citizens have actually seen a lion, elephant, or kudu in the wild. During October of 2007, Mr. Daniel Nzengy'a arranged for students in his Wildlife Management class to spend a long weekend at Mana Pools National Park. In addition to taking game drives and photographing animals that ventured into camp, the students interviewed wildlife professionals involved in the day-to-day operation of a national park and accompanied these government biologists on a lion-tracking expedition. The trip was not a luxury outing: students prepared their own food, slept on the ground, and, using field guides, served as their own safari leaders. But a good time was had by all (especially Chris and Ab), and the Wildlife students returned to campus with deeper perspective and a renewed dedication to their academic/professional objectives. If you visit Africa University, or if you know someone who may go there as part of a VIM team, you might give the Dean of Agriculture and Natural Resources enough money to support a National Park fieldtrip. Contributions between $100 and $500U.S. would go a long way towards financing one or more such class activities.

Mana Pools Fieldtrip, 2007 (Student-Photographer Elvis Gushumbe)

vice project, students (especially Shona-speakers from Old Mutare) could interview resource users and ask in non-threatening ways about their activities on the A.U. campus. (The Terry-and-Mugave model demonstrates that such an approach can work.) This initial survey could develop into a program that would monitor the extraction of gold, firewood, medicinal plants, and bush meat. Such information could document the importance of campus natural resources in the lives of local people; we could learn how crowded the "lifeboat" really is.

Properly supervised, such student research could generate formal scientific papers, particularly if FANR were joined in the monitoring project by other Faculties. These publications, in turn, could create significant extramural interest and support (see 3. below). In time, the local folks who exploit campus resources could participate in drafting A.U. harvest regulations and could be empowered to develop sustainable strategies for conserving the resources upon which they depend. Eventually, some sections of the campus might be declared as resource-extraction areas: get your permit, report your take, and help A.U. renew the good things that you acquire from her natural bounty. Other areas might be placed off limits to all except University scientists. Outside visitors could be encouraged to explore the beauty of some campus landscapes and to participate in a variety of ongoing research projects. We know this can work, at least on a small scale, because we would be delighted to join a VIM Team of taxonomists and nature photographers. And we can see no limits to the amount of fun that might be had!

3. Wildlands conservation: Outside help. Your four authors have discussed this matter for many hours, and we are convinced that substantial outside help for a campus conservation program is available. For example, FANR could draft a proposal to the American Fulbright Foundation, requesting a one-year teaching/research Fellow in sustainable exploitation of natural resources. This might be followed up by asking the Harare embassies of G-20 nations about the availability of Peace Corps-type work-

ers trained in environmental research and education. We would petition the United Methodist Board of Education (GBHEM) to fund an additional full-time instructor in natural resources; such a position might also be supported by the General Board of Global Ministries. Because United Methodism (and A.U.) has always maintained a strongly ecumenical outlook, we would also seek help from pan-Methodist and other faith-based communities. (In particular, Chris and Ab would like to ask that the Palmetto Conference of the African Methodist Episcopal Church support an A.U. scholarship for a first-year student in Natural Resources.)

In December of 2007, Ab told his boss and long-time friend, Dr. Fanuel Tagwira, that he was embarrassed by the inability of the South Carolina team to invent more creative stewardship strategies. And Professor Tagwira, formal as ever, asked "Professor Abercrombie" whether he had really learned the lesson about making two blades of grass grow where only one had grown before. That was an important moment; we had recognized that our suggestions were simplistic and incomplete, that they were easy to write and difficult to implement. And we had been forced to admit that gloom and doom had tempted us towards restful resignation; we had to confess that, like Old Bushy in this book's foreword, we had been buffeted a bit by hunger and fear. Nevertheless, as Boss Tagwira reminded us, we cherish a Gospel that turns forward, toward the future, with joy. As we say back in South Carolina, *DUM SPIRO, SPERO.* Therefore, since we do in fact breathe, we do in fact hope — for at least two blades of grass!

"Feed my sheep."
John 21:17

123

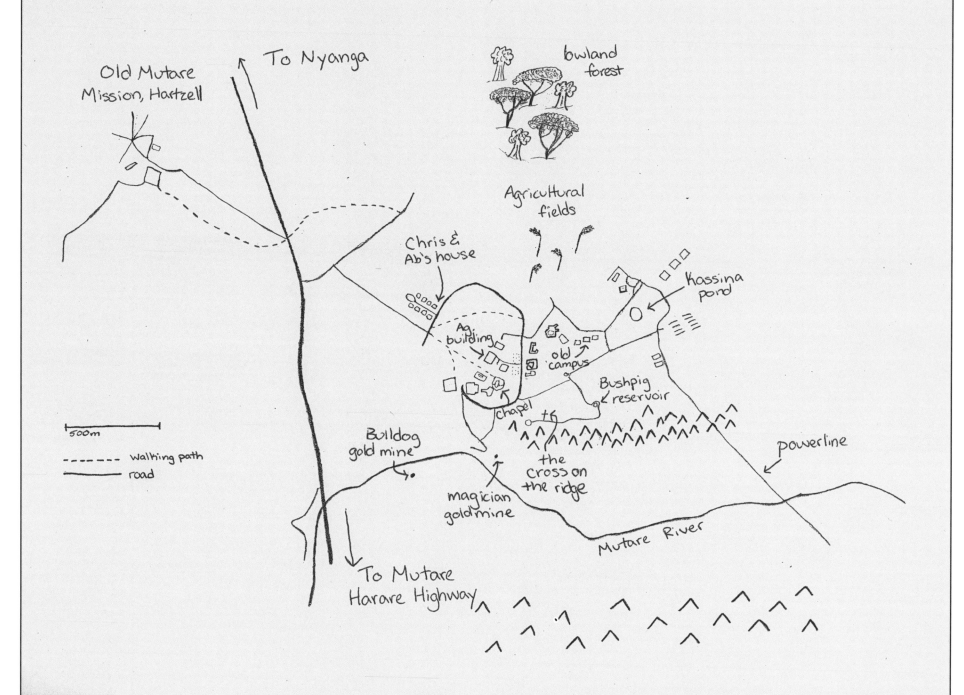